ANTHOKINETICS

THE PHYSIOLOGY AND ECOLOGY OF FLORAL MOVEMENTS

BY

G. W. GOLDSMITH

AND

A. L. HAFENRICHTER

CARNEGIE INSTITUTION OF WASHINGTON

March, 1932

CARNEGIE INSTITUTION OF WASHINGTON
PUBLICATION No. 420

W. F. ROBERTS COMPANY
NATIONAL ENGRAVING CO.
WASHINGTON, D. C.

CONTENTS

ILLUSTRATIONS

PLATES

TEXT-FIGURES

ANTHOKINETICS

THE PHYSIOLOGY AND ECOLOGY OF FLORAL MOVEMENTS

BY

G. W. GOLDSMITH and A. L. HAFENRICHTER

I

INTRODUCTION

SCOPE AND AIMS OF THE WORK

Plant movements have long offered an attractive field of study to physiologists and ecologists. Not only are the observed movements important in themselves as an expression of the vital activity of organisms the life processes of which are commonly not conspicuous or easily mensurable, but an understanding of the phenomenon is also important to ecology and morphology, and has direct bearing on the more general and fundamental problems of plant physiology. Movement, as one of the many adjustments of the plant to the environment, affords a useful means of study, since it is a response of the plant that can be quantitatively determined. The study of flower movements—anthokinetics—also has a direct and important bearing on the ecology of flowers.

The movements exhibited, the organs involved, the importance, variation and evolution within the taxonomic and ecological groups, adjustments to the environment, and nature of the stimuli, all are of much ecological significance. Physiologically the relation of movement to respiration, transpiration, photosynthesis, growth, irritability, tissue mechanics, permeability, and osmotic relations of the tissues is fundamental.

Movements may be divided into those of growth and those of turgidity. Each group may be autonomic or paratonic, depending upon whether the stimuli are internal or external. Autonomic growth movements include nutation, twining and nastic bending; paratonic growth movements are the tropistic ones. Autonomic turgidity movements are known to occur rarely in leaflets; the paratonic category includes the movements of stomata, and those which occur in response to light and contact (Palladin and Livingston, 1922). Most flower movements are commonly included under nastic bending, although individual instances have been shown to belong elsewhere (Pfeffer 1873, Hendricks 1919).

Flower movements frequently occur in species widely scattered through the taxonomic groups, as has been indicated by Hansgirg. That such movements are of value is shown in the work of Hofmeister, Kerner, Haberlandt, and many others. Floral movements may result in the protection of the organs against unfavorable weather conditions, the admittance of pollinators adapted in structure and activity to the flower, or the maximum floral display within a limited period favorable for the particular pollinators concerned. The vari-

3

ability and frequency of flower movements indicate their ecological importance and evolutionary and adaptative development.

The present study was primarily undertaken in the field, from the ecological standpoint. The ecological aspects being so intimately connected with the physiological, laboratory and greenhouse studies were used to further the work. An attempt was made first to study the field behavior of the flowers and to ascertain its ecological importance. Studies of the nature of the stimulating factors were carried out in the field and supplemented in the laboratory under carefully controlled conditions which permitted a comprehensive study of the mechanics of the tissues involved.

RÉSUMÉ OF PREVIOUS INVESTIGATIONS

Since interest in plant movements has been general among botanists from the time of the early development of the science to the present day, the literature on the subject is both extensive and scattered. The following is designed to furnish a brief account of the general progress in this field, but not as a complete historical treatment. The early work was largely descriptive, but soon included a number of species in which movement was considered in relation to some metabolic process. Study of the qualitative and quantitative effects of the stimulating factors was followed by investigation of the mechanics of the tissues involved, and application of such results as became available from work on other plant organs. The bibliography appended contains references to the more important investigations, and particularly to those of significance in the present research.

Linné (1751) observed flower movements and classified them according to the time of day and the weather conditions prevailing at the opening and closing periods.

De Saussure (1822) studied the respiration of various flowers. He found the respiration higher than that in leaves, the maximum recorded for the flower being over 24 times greater. Floral respiration was increased by sunlight or an elevation of temperature. An inflorescence of *Arum maculatum* weighing 74 grams used 965 cc. of oxygen in 24 hours. Studies of the oxygen consumption of various portions showed that the most rapid respiration took place in the essential organs. The respiration rate was greatest at the time of the opening of the flowers, and was likewise high at the time of fertilization. Flowers of *Passiflora serratifolia* were found to consume 6 times their volume of oxygen in 12 hours when in bud, 12 times during the early opening stage, and 7 times when the flower was old.

De Candolle (1835), as a result of illuminating *Mirabilis jalapa* at night and shading it by day, concluded that light was the stimulating factor in movements, although the effect was not a simple one.

Dutrochet (1836) believed that the opening of flowers was due to turgescence and the filling of the fibrous tissues with oxygen.

Hoffmann (1850) emphasized the effect of temperature on the movement of flowers of *Oenothera biennis,* and leaves of *Oxalis rosea, Tolpis barbata,* and *Eschscholtzia.* He was unable to change by artificial light the daily behavior rhythm of leaves of *Tolpis barbata* and *Oxalis tetraphylla,* and of flowers of *Lotus peregrinus* and *Oenothera lindleyana.* Leaves of *Oxalis tetraphylla* and *Mimosa pudica,* as well as flowers of *Tolpis barbata* and *Oenothera lindleyana,* behaved normally when submerged in water. No effect of humid or dry air on the behavior of *Oxalis rosea* flowers could be seen.

Kabsch (1862) studied the physiological effects of carbon dioxide, hydrogen, nitrogen, nitrous oxide, and oxygen, on leaves and flowers of *Berberis.* Sensitivity was destroyed temporarily by atmospheres containing 20 to 25 per cent carbon dioxide, and permanently by 60 to 70 per cent. An atmosphere containing 50 per cent hydrogen retarded the rate of reaction, while an atmosphere of nitrogen produced no effect. Nitrous oxide caused erratic movements with closing in 1.5 to 2 minutes, followed by death. The effects of oxygen were quicker but otherwise similar.

Hofmeister (1868) reported that the development of the embryo was profoundly affected by the position of the maturing fruit.

Royer (1868) attributed floral movement to heat and turgescence, and ascribed to light a secondary rôle. Movement in leaves was considered to be quite different from that in flowers because the presence of chlorophyll renders light an effective stimulus to movement. Temperature was thought to affect directly the concentration of the cell sap and thus produce the movement of the floral parts. Experimental work was reported upon a number of flowers, including *Tulipa, Crocus, Taraxacum, Convolvulus, Mirabilis, Datura,* and many others. Diuturnal flowers could be made ephemeral by intensifying the conditions that promote rapid desiccation, and ephemeral flowers could be made more persistent by an increase in moisture.

Sachs (1863, 1874, 1887) described various nutations. He found that light sensitized the leaves of *Mimosa pudica,* and that darkness produced a stasis. Light was considered of great importance in flower movement, tulip and crocus being exceptional in responding to temperature changes. Living protoplasm was shown to be essential, and the actual movement was assumed to be caused by contractile cells as well as by turgescence.

Pfeffer (1873, 1875, 1907) made detailed studies on the physiology both of leaf and flower movement, which he regarded as similar. By measuring the distance between lines marked on the moving parts of flowers of crocus, tulip, dandelion and others, he showed that the side toward which the movement took place did not elongate as rapidly as the opposite one. Measurements upon *Crocus vernus* while opening showed an average increase in length of .2 per cent on the outside and 2.4 per cent on the inside in the region 3 mm. long that was most actively concerned in the opening. This produced a curvature with a radius of 15 to 30 mm. By means of temperature and light variations, opening and closing were made to alternate repeatedly, if a period of recovery were allowed between the reactions. In the case of crocus, the flowers were opened and closed 8 times in one day. A temperature variation of 5 degrees produced a reaction in 8 minutes; one of 10 degrees in 3 minutes. Similar movements could be produced by these temperatures with the flowers submerged in water. Perianth parts of tulip showed an equilibrium position corresponding to the temperature. The temperature maxima and minima beyond which reaction did not occur were found to be different for the various species.

Temperature stimuli were effective in opening the flowers of *Oxalis* and of *Taraxacum* at night only when the flowers had first been kept in darkness, and then only after time had been allowed for the effect of this previous light condition to disappear. Most composites with active flowers opened if warmed in the morning, but did not respond to similar treatment at night. *Calendula* and other composites responded to light, the vigor of the reaction varying with the time elapsed since the last response in an opposite direction. Light was considered a cause rather than a regulator of movement. Darkness accelerated growth but considerable time must have elapsed before this acceleration was perceptible. Tulip and crocus flowers were exceptional in responding to temperature rather than to light, but they were opened or closed by a sudden great increase or decrease in light in spite of antagonistic temperature stimuli.

Detailed studies by means of recording apparatus showed that two classes of leaf behavior might be distinguished, depending on whether the response followed the stimulus quickly, as in *Mimosa*, or only after a period of several hours, as in *Phaseolus*. Leaves of the latter showed a periodic movement independent of the dark and light periods to which the plant had been subjected. Short-period rhythmic movements could be established in the leaves of *Albizzia lophantha* by exposing the plant to 6-hour periods of light and darkness, but intervals of 18 hours did not modify the usual daily periodic movement. Both these genera showed daily periodic leaf movements in darkness.

The filaments in flowers of *Centaurea* shortened when stimulated mechanically. This was due to a change in turgescence resulting from a change in osmotic concentration rather than in permeability, some of the cell fluids escaping into the intercellular spaces and thus producing the reaction. In general, temperature changes could not account for the observed alterations in osmotic pressure. Light was considered of great importance in leaf movements, acting directly through its effect upon the chlorophyll.

Balfour (1875), in discussing flower movement, emphasized spontaneous periodic behavior.

Kerner (1876) pointed out the importance of the position of the flower and fruit in the movements observed.

De Vries (1877, 1884) showed that when the growing organs of a plant were plasmolyzed they were shortened, but recovered their length if placed in water.

Darwin and Darwin (1880) reported detailed studies of plant movements and pointed out their significance to the species concerned. Leaf positions are of advantage to the species because of the protection afforded and, being general among plants in varying degrees, are material for natural selection and development. Differential growth and turgescence produced the movements. As De Vries had shown, a differential turgescence frequently preceded differential growth.

Vöchting (1882, 1890, 1908) in studying flower movement in several species, found that the concept of geotropism could not be satisfactorily applied because of the frequent changes in both directions between the positive and negative types. Seeds of *Papaver* did not develop normally in fruit secured in an abnormal position. The presence of the bud on the peduncle was found necessary for the normal movements of this organ. Such movements depended on the complete system rather than on any single part, as was shown by the fact that the removal of the inflorescence of *Brassica rapa* caused changes in the position of the leaves. Differential growth produced movement, at least in *Anemone*.

Hansgirg (1890, 1896, 1904) listed many species that showed movement, and described their behavior. He classified the various movements as gamotropic and carpotropic, according to their mechanism and purpose. Gamotropic movements occurred in the ovary, petals, or stamens, and were believed to result in the protection of the essential organs of the flower, or the promotion of cross pollination. Carpotropic movements affected the calyx, involucre, or the position of the flower at different stages in the life history. Gamo-

tropic movements, which take place as the result of differential growth
(epinasty and hyponasty), were stimulated by changes in light and
temperature. Carpotropic movements were assumed to be due to
growth, but the occurrence of differential growth was considered still
unproved. Humidity was regarded as an important stimulating
factor.

Wieler (1893) studied the amount of bleeding from cut flowers
under various air pressures as a measure of the transpirational water
present. The osmotic pressure of the tissue and the physical conditions of the cell walls were considered of great importance in flower
movement. As Sachs showed, in cut flowers there was a relation between the position of the flower parts and the transpirational water.
A similar relation between flower movement and foliar transpiration
did not hold.

Oltmanns (1895) distinguished between such flowers as *Lactuca
perennis, Tragopogon brevirostris, Leontodon taraxacum,* and *Mirabilis jalapa,* which open in the morning and close on bright days not
later than 10 A.M., and *Bellis perennis* and other composites that
also open in the morning but do not close until late afternoon. In
the first type an increase of temperature or light intensity hastened
closing so that, as Pfeffer later found true for leaves, these factors
produced either opening or closing, depending on the intensity. These
were grouped as "early closers." The "late closers," typified by
Bellis perennis, correspond in reaction with nyctotropic leaves.
Closure resulted in the afternoon from a fall in light intensity and
temperature. A dark period increased the sensitivity to light, and
previous exposure to light was found to increase the speed of closure
in darkness. Oltmanns emphasized the effect of light as a stimulus
in flower movement.

Kerner and Oliver (1895) stressed the importance of absorbed
radiant energy, and in this connection considered highly important
the presence of anthocyanin pigments in the outer epidermis of the
floral parts. Since, as Pfeffer showed, the direct effect of temperature upon the concentration of the cell sap was not sufficient to
explain movement as due to changes in turgescence, floral movements
were considered to be directly connected with the stimulation of the
protoplasm. In ephemerals, where closure meant the death of the
flower, water loss was doubtless an important factor.

Jost (1895, 1898, 1902, 1904) studied the movements both of
leaves and flowers. He found that leaves kept in darkness while the
rest of the plant was exposed to the daily light changes showed the
same rhythm as the exposed leaves. He believed that the action of
darkness on leaf movement was directly attributable to the effect on
the chlorophyll. *Mimosa* leaves were sensitive both to heating and

cooling, and were more sensitive at lower temperatures. Flowers of *Tulipa, Crocus,* and *Taraxacum* were stimulated by sufficiently high temperatures to open and then close. Opening and closing in *Tulipa* and *Crocus* were almost exclusively in response to temperature. Growth in tulip flowers, as measured microscopically, was greatly and quickly increased by changing from 11° to 18° C., but fell in the next hour to approximately the original, as was also the case in 4-5 hours at 18° constant, the temperature change acting as a stimulus. *Impatiens* leaves showed greater elongation on the upper surface while assuming the sleep position, but no differential growth while resuming the day position, other causes being operative in this movement. Results for *Leontodon* showed an increased growth in the morning but practically none during the night. Flowers opened at temperatures above the growth maximum, and closed at those below the growth minimum. No floral movements occurred in *Taraxacum officinale, Leontodon hastilis,* and similar flowers, in atmospheres of oxygen or carbon dioxide. Wiesner's studies showed that the opening of the flowers of *Anagallis* resulted from changes in water distribution. *Tulipa* and *Taraxacum* belong to the "free closers" category of Oltmanns, for shortly after opening they close under constant external conditions. Jost employed temperatures of 18° C. or more, but did not take into account humidity, which was probably very low.

Farmer (1902) reported a careful study of the mechanism involved in the movement of tulip flowers. Young flowers were found to open in response to an increase in temperature and to close following a decrease. He considered it doubtful whether growth could be responsible for this behavior. Near the base of the perianth he located cells that produced the movement by undergoing changes in turgescence. It was noted that median longitudinal sections of a flower, when placed in water, became more strongly curved, corresponding to the movement of closure. When these turgid sections were put in a plasmolyzing solution of 3-4 per cent potassium nitrate, a movement corresponding to that of opening occurred quickly. By making the proper changes between water and potassium nitrate solution these movements could be produced repeatedly in a single section. Similar sections fixed in the closed position by means of alcohol opened in either salt solution or water, but could not be closed again. Tissue near the base of the perianth showed large tangentially arranged intercellular spaces so that alteration in the state of turgescence and the size of the cells sufficient to produce the flower movements observed could take place without a shearing action.

Burgerstein (1902), studying the behavior of the flowers of *Tulipa* and *Crocus,* found that at a constant high temperature the rates of the opening movements were first accelerated and then re-

tarded; no closure resulted. The floral movements of *Crocus vernus*
C. luteus, and *Tulipa gesneriana,* took place in atmospheres of oxygen,
hydrogren, and carbon dioxide, in atmospheric pressures reduced to
20 mm., and in solutions of salts below the plasmolyzing concentration.
Since flowers open and close at temperatures outside of the growth
range, growth played an accompanying but secondary part. Conard
(1903) described the opening and closing of several species of water
lilies and found that the time of floral opening advanced with age
from morning to afternoon in certain species.

Wiedersheim (1904) decided that differential growth had not
been found completely to explain photonastic and thermonastic movements. It was in recognition of this that Jost assumed a connected
chain of reactions resulting from the initiating stimulus. Growth
processes were followed by marking the active regions with lines of
India ink and measuring the elongation by means of a micrometer.
Leaves of *Impatiens parviflora, Crocus luteus,* and flowers of *Tulipa*
were studied. *Impatiens* showed a transitory growth, appearing first
on the upper surface, and preceding movement; a similar relation was
observed on the two sides of the perianth of tulip flowers. The accelerated growth in tulips persisted for 60 minutes after stimulation.
Measurements showed a total increase of inner surface over outer of
7.2 per cent in one case and 5.9 per cent in a second. This differential
rate occurred in response to temperature changes which were not of
apparent difference on the two surfaces. When moving parts were
prevented from carrying out their normal nutations, a limited growth
still appeared, showing that the curvature could not be of importance
as a stimulus for the reverse reaction, as Fitting supposed. It was
concluded that movements result from growth processes on opposing
sides of the active structure which differ in their time of subsidence.

Hensel (1905) carried out experimental studies in field and greenhouse by heating, shading and watering. The results of these experiments, together with field observations, led her to the conclusion
that temperature is the stimulating factor in the movements of most
flowers observed. On the basis of flower behavior, she classified plants
into day-bloomers and night-bloomers. In the first group were placed
hemeranthous flowers which open only during the day, but for two
or more days successively, and ephemeral-hemeranthous flowers which
open for all or part of but one day. In the second group were included nyctanthous flowers which open for two or more successive
nights, and ephemeral-nyctanthous ones which open for but one
night. The movements of hemeranthous and nyctanthous flowers
were found to be stimulated by temperature changes. Ephemeral
flowers were found to be prevented from opening by low temperatures, but after opening low temperatures prevented collapse.

Stoppel (1910, 1916, 1926), Stoppel and Kniep (1910), and Stoppel and Trumpf (1922), have reported detailed and exhaustive studies of leaf and flower movement. Plants of *Calendula arvensis* and *Bellis perennis* were kept in a basement room in which the temperature variation was slight and subjected to varying periods of darkness and artificial illumination. Flowers of *Calendula* carried out their usual 24-hour cycle of movement when exposed to alternate light and dark periods of 12 hours. In darkness an autonomic opening and closing occurred in the usual daily cycles. Constant illumination produced first opening and later closing, the autonomic movements displayed being slow and erratic. Flowers subjected to alternate light and dark periods of 6 hours or less exhibited only the usual autonomic rhythm. The normal daily rhythm of autonomic movement was not affected by the period to which the flower had previously been exposed, but the time at which the darkened flower assumed a given floral stage depended upon the time of the preceding dark period.

Autonomic movements were greater in darkness than in light, but no periodic movements were observed in the open flower. Darkness was thought to sensitize rather than stimulate; the maximum amplitude of movement could be induced in *Calendula* flowers after 24 hours in darkness. Light and dark periods to which the leaves had been exposed produced no effect on the movement of the flowers. Opening or closing when once initiated could not be reversed by changing the stimuli to those usually causing the opposite reaction. Light showed an inhibiting effect upon the buds of *Calendula*. A given light period that suppressed the normal daily periodic movements of the flower subjected to it in the afternoon, was without effect when administered in the morning. The season was also effective in sensitizing to light, the best curves being obtained during the winter months. In weak light or darkness the flowers of *Bellis perennis* did not open, but in bright light they carried out their daily rhythm with gradually decreasing amplitude. In 6-hour light and dark periods the flowers opened with the light and closed with darkness, but when subjected to 4-hour or 1-hour periods they merely followed their usual daily rhythm.

In a detailed series of studies on the leaf movement of *Phaseolus multiflorus,* Stoppel found a simple relation with temperature, the leaves rising when heated and drooping when cooled. The leaves of seedlings grown in darkness displayed the usual movements, showing that no after effects of light and dark periods were present in normal plants. In Iceland, under conditions of continuous sunlight, leaf movements were similar to those observed in Germany, differing only in amplitude. Pfeffer (1911) found that the leaf movements of *Phaseolus* were not modified by mechanical resistance. The mechanism of this movement was active without bending or torsion, and increased in power when resistance was added.

Ulrich (1911) reported the results of detailed studies of the leaf movements of several species of *Oxalidaceae*, finding light an important factor for all. *Oxalis bupleurifolia* exhibited leaf depression in .9 seconds after stimulation by an electric current, a rest period of 7.5 seconds, and a recovery requiring 6.5 minutes. After a second stimulation, reactions up to five in number followed with no further external excitation. Successive mechanical stimulations produced reactions of increasing amplitude. The leaves of *Averrhoa carambola* assumed the night position by a series of depressions followed by partial recoveries. Electrical stimuli were cumulative so that a current too weak to produce a reaction would do so if repeated, and then successive reactions followed without further stimulation. Other species of *Oxalidaceae* showed varying degrees of sensitivity. Periodic movements corresponding to the usual daily cycle were often evident in darkness, persisting until the leaves became partially etiolated and nearly dead.

Strasburger, Jost, Schenck, and Karsten (1912) ascribe flower movements to differential growth. The stimulus was found to be temperature change in the case of tulip, crocus and others; and a change in light intensity for the flowers of composites, *Silene noctiflora,* and others. The protection of the essential parts from unfavorable weather conditions, or the promotion of pollination were assigned as the cause.

Pringsheim (1912) has summarized the work on plant movements. Light and temperature were regarded as the important stimulating factors, and differential growth was considered the operative cause of flower movement in many cases. A daily periodic cycle of sensitivity to stimuli was observed, but periodic behavior varied markedly in different species. Flower movements usually coincided with the activities of insects effective as pollinating agents of the species. Irritability was considered to be only the operation of various known chemical and physical laws, some applications of which were suggested. The term irritability in the present sense of the word could then be dropped.

Haberlandt (1914) summarized the results of earlier workers. He divided movements into (1) release of tissue tensions; (2) growth movements with or without the aid of special organs, which may be autonomous (nutations) or tropistic (induced by external stimuli); (3) special motor tissue movements, due to differential growth or turgor changes. He supposed that different families of flowering plants had evolved different mechanisms of movement, since it was known that the various characteristic structures had been developed independently. Thus while curvature in the *Cucurbitaceae, Passi-floraceae, Papilionaceae,* and *Vitaceae* was found to be the result of differential growth, in the *Sapindaceae* it was due to osmotic changes similar to those described by Pfeffer in flowers of *Centaurea.*

Iljin (1914) found the osmotic concentration of the epidermal cells of leaves relatively constant, as determined by the threshold of plasmolysis induced by potassium nitrate solutions. The guard cells showed considerable variation, but the parenchyma resembled the epidermis in showing a constant concentration. Ursprung and Blum (1916) checked their method of determination of the osmotic concentration in cells by the changes in volume occurring in various solutions, against the results obtained by plasmolysis and found them in agreement.

Bose (1916), and Bose and Prassana (1925), as a result of minute studies of plant movement, considered response to be due to protoplasmic irritability. The rate of conduction in *Mimosa* did not agree with the water currents in the vessels, as was believed by Ricca. Romell (1918) reported the results of a study on the periodic variation in sap pressure from a cut stem of *Brassica oleracea.* This author believed that movements were due to irritability, the stimulus being changes in root pressure in the case of *B. oleracea.* Pfeffer's results on the osmotic concentration of the cell sap and Pringsheim's ideas of irritability were discounted. Hendricks (1919, 1923) showed that for *Phaseolus multiflorus* and *Tiniaria convolvulus* the maximum twining movement occurred only after the period of greatest elongation of the internodes. Torsion was followed by a slight reverse at the time of lignification. Schulz (1921) discovered a relation between the floral and geotropic movements in *Papaver.* Wiggans (1921) confirmed the results of Iljin, finding the concentration of the epidermal cells of the leaf relatively constant, and that of the guard cells with periodic variation. By the plasmolytic method, using calcium chloride solutions, concentrations in pigmented epidermal cells were found to vary from .16 to .60 molar in *Cyclamen, Iresine,* and *Beta.*

Davy de Virville and Obaton (1922) found temperature of prime effect in the opening of the ephemeral flowers, *Helianthemum guttatum, Anagallis arvensis,* and *Phaenopus murialis,* with light and humidity of minor importance. In a later study of the same year they extended their conclusions to a number of species of diurnal and nocturnal flowers. These types were shown to be less sensitive to temperature than the ephemerals, and were affected little if at all by light and humidity; these conclusions were emphasized again in 1923. Sensitivity to temperature changes decreased with the age of the flower and with the advance of the season. From the effects of

temperature on the development of the bud, there appeared to be
a relation between the preceding temperature and the number of
flowers open on a plant for any one day.

Lundegårdh (1922) recorded photographically the movements
of the coleoptile of *Avena sativa* when stimulated by light. The
movement showed points of maximum and minimum amplitude with
increasing light intensity, indicating that the curvature was not due
to a simple process; with unilateral illumination the growth curve
was found to be nearly the mirror image for that of bending. In
phototropism, time and intensity factors must be considered as well
as the light absorption by the internal tissues.

Palladin and Livingston (1922) have given an inclusive classi-
fication of plant movements: (1) growth movements which occur
in organs undergoing the secondary growth, that is, enlargement; this
group includes tropisms and the epinastic and hyponastic movements
of flowers and leaves; (2) turgidity movements include stomatal
movements, sleep movements of leaves, contact movements of *Mimosa,* and variation movements of *Desmodium gyrans* described by
Hofmeister. Growth is enlargement for which turgidity is essential.
Measurements showed that differential growth in response to light and
temperature stimulation produced the opening and closing of flowers.

Suessenguth (1922) has made an important and detailed contri-
bution to the knowledge of the mechanism of movement, regarding
differential pressure as its cause. Carbon dioxide in concentration of
30 per cent changed leaves of *Albizzia* and other forms from day to
night position, either in light or darkness, while low concentrations
(5 per cent) inhibited normal reactions to darkening. This seemed
to be due to the swelling effect of carbon dioxide on the colloids.
Chloroform, ether, and illuminating gas tended to prevent the usual
daily movements, the former causing *Mimosa* leaves to assume the
night position because the general permeability to water resulted in
the loss of differential turgescence. Hydrogen, nitrogen, and oxygen,
not being ionized, showed little or no effect upon movement, and
this was also true where the air was ionized by means of uranium.
Relatively turgid cells lost water under the influence of light, relatively flaccid ones gained water. Stomatal transpiration was of no
importance in leaf movement, the behavior of the guard cells not
being correlated with it. Transpiration was believed to be significant only in the portion most actively concerned in movement,
and since stomatal condition had little or no effect upon leaf behavior
there was probably no noteworthy translocation of solutions. Root
pressure had no effect, but it was thought that respirational carbon
dioxide might produce swelling of the colloids. It was concluded that

interactions due rather to colloids than to crystalloids controlled the water relations and hence the movements of the leaf.

Brauner (1922, 1924, 1926) obtained a close correlation between growth and curvature in the coleoptile of oats. He believed that light, by increasing the permeability of the cells, as shown by electrical conductivity determinations and plasmolysis with sodium nitrate solution, furthers the conduction of growth-inhibiting materials. Light rather than temperature was considered to be the stimulating factor for leaves of *Phaseolus multiflorus*. Saxton (1923) described the leaf movements of a number of common Indian plants. Most of these movements required 40 to 45 minutes and occurred in sunlight. Pranchard and Waight (1923) found that the irritability of pteridophytes, as measured by the presentation time, depended on the stage of development of the fronds.

Skene (1924) regarded temperature as the usual causal factor in the opening of flowers, although light was effective in some instances. Closure was believed to be an automatic reversal of the opening process, and differential growth responsible for the actual movement. Basically, movement was explained by rhythm which was induced, accentuated, or modified by external factors, the rhythm itself having been caused by inherent factors or by a summation of external ones. Night closing was for the protection of the essential organs against moisture, but the advantage of day closure was obscure. No flowers were known to respond to changes in humidity. Opdenbosch (1924) found that in flowers of *Tulipa, Ornithogalum, Eschscholtzia californica,* and *E. douglasi,* light had no perceptible effect, but that high temperatures hastened and low temperatures retarded the opening-closing process.

Snow (1924, 1925) studied conduction of stimuli in the leaves and stems of *Mimosa spegazzini* and *M. pudica* by following the spread of stains in the tissues. It was concluded that the spread of a stimulating substance through the xylem accounted for the conduction in the stem, as shown by Ricca, but this could not be the case in the leaves where the stimulus conduction does not always agree in speed or direction with the water current.

Trumpf (1924) studied the effect of light on the growth of stems and leaves. Red and blue light affected the growth of the stem and leaf in opposite ways. Conduction of light effects between organs could not be shown, but such effects did not occur during narcosis and at low temperatures, and were regarded as dependent on photochemical action rather than on irritability. There was a light requirement for leaf movement in *Phaseolus multiflorus* independent of that necessary for chlorophyll formation. Ursprung and Blum (1924) followed the turgor changes in the guard cells of *Convallaria majalis* and in the root tip of *Vicia faba* by means of volume changes in cells placed in various solutions. In the curving zone of the roots of *V. faba* and in the stems of *Tradescantia* the osmotic pressure was similar on the opposing sides, but the turgor pressure and suction force were greater on the convex than on the concave side. Guttenberg (1925) described the mechanism involved in the movements of the leaves of *Dionaea muscipula*. Osmotic pressure in the tissue fluid was observed to increase to 14 atmospheres under stimulus. The mesophyll cells increased in size as did those of the lower epidermis, but the cells of the upper epidermis did not enlarge, and movement resulted in consequence.

Nuernbergk (1925) made a detailed study of sleep positions occurring in leaves during the day. He distinguished a "light sleep" and a "heat sleep," the former being a response to the shorter waves of the visible spectrum, and the latter to the total energy absorbed. These movements were repressed by temperatures above the optimal, but showed no relation to stomatal movement and transpiration, though of advantage, the author believed, in placing the chloroplasts in reduced illumination. Küster (1927) reported detailed researches by the plasmolytic method. Injury to the cells may cause plasmolysis, but this can be checked by the recovery of the plasmolyzed cells when placed in water.

Ivanow (1927) determined the water content of the petals of *Paeonia, Rosa,* and *Papaver* to be 81.1 to 84.7 per cent. The hygroscopic water of petals from various species was found to vary from 10.02 to 14.25 per cent of the dry weight. The ash content of petals was very high, the maximum being 20 per cent, and the transpiration rate was also greater than that of leaves. Höfler (1928) made a detailed study of plasmolysis induced by solutions of salts of various metals and concluded that the endoplast was of great importance in varying the form of plasmolysis. Beck (1927, 1929) studied plasmolysis by the methods of Ursprung and Blum and found the speed of plasmolysis and deplasmolysis different. Cane sugar was recommended as a plasmolyzing material, as deplasmolysis did not occur and considerable time could be allowed for observations.

Andrews (1929) found that crocus and tulip flowers opened at temperature increases of .2° to 1° C., but the rate of movement under these circumstances was slow. Crocus flowers could be opened and closed many times in rapid succession and were more sensitive to temperature changes than those of tulip. Nigel (1926) has shown that stimuli may be transmitted through water film. Kienholz (1927) recorded a cessation of growth and even a shrinkage in stem length of several Philippine species during the daylight period. This behavior did not coincide with the evaporation rate as measured by an atmometer, but more nearly with the light variation.

PRESENT KNOWLEDGE OF THE PHYSIOLOGY AND
MECHANISM INVOLVED

In the course of the observational and experimental studies outlined above, a knowledge of the physiological mechanism of the processes concerned in flower movement has gradually developed, furthered materially by the results of researches in other fields. Since the work of Pfeffer, showing that a differential elongation on the two surfaces of the perianth accompanied the opening and closing of flowers of tulip, crocus, calendula, daisy and others, the mechanism involved has been generally accepted as growth. Pfeffer's use of this term is inclusive, as may be seen from his definition, "The term growth may be used to indicate all formative processes leading to a change of shape or of structure." Enlargement is the usual measure of growth from which our quantitive knowledge of this complex process is obtained. Few quantitative estimations of the cell-division or material-deposition phases of the growth process are applicable to higher plant forms. De Vries (1877) demonstrated the intimate relation between growth and turgidity, while Pfeffer's work brought out clearly the importance of the osmotic concentration of the cell sap and of the permeability of the investing membranes of the cells.

Extensive research on the osmotic relations of tissues and tissue fluids has been carried out. Among recent investigators, Dixon (1914), Atkins (1916), and Harris and his associates (1916, 1917), have shown a relation between the concentration of the tissue fluids and the habitat and functions of the plant. Osmotic concentration bears an important but complicated relation to the activities of plants, but it has become evident that it affords but incomplete insight into the physiological activities of tissues.

Recently Ursprung (1923) and Molz (1926) have taken into consideration the elastic force of the cell in the study of suction force, or the amount of osmotic pressure available above that necessary for the maintenance of turgidity. The results differ in varying degrees from those of osmotic concentration, but they have not been related more intimately to plant activities. Investigations of irritability, though extensive, have not contributed much to knowledge of the mechanism of flower movements, beyond the details of the time and intensity relations of stimulus and response. Verworn (1912) has given a complete discusion of the studies in this field.

Of equal importance with osmotic concentration is the permeability of the structures in which the solutions are enclosed. Stiles (1925) has given an excellent summary of results and a complete bibliography. Quantitative measurements of permeability are difficult because of frequent changes both in this condition of the tissue and in the substances present. There can be no doubt of the intimate rela-

tion between growth, turgidity, osmotic pressure, and permeability.
Thus far conclusions applicable to flower movement are few, beyond
the knowledge that changes in permeability occur frequently in plant
tissues, show periodic fluctuations, and affect growth and movement
through turgidity conditions. Whether or not such changes in permeability as have been measured are sufficient to account for turgidity
alterations and the resultant movements seems doubtful (Blackman and Paine 1918), but there can be little question that they are
a contributory cause. MacDougal (1920) has discussed the significance of hydration in growth phenomena, and related it to the composition, acidity, physical state, and other conditions of the cell.

Flower movement is not attributable to the primary phase of
growth, since actively dividing cells occur in the early development
of the bud rather than in the flower, and also because of the rapidity
and frequency of movement in response to stimuli. Turgidity of the
tissue actively concerned in movement is of great importance in the
flower, and in final analysis depends upon the water relations and imbibitional conditions of the tissue. Some of the characteristics of
growth, and even a type of periodicity, may be exhibited by colloids of
comparatively simple composition.

Contractions are not unknown in growth processes, for Bose
(1916), and recently Dowling (1923) and Kienholz (1927), have
shown that a rhythmic elongation and contraction may occur. Studies
sufficiently accurate to ascertain whether flowers in process of opening and closing exhibit a similar rhythm have not been reported. The
growth process occurring in flower movement is to be connected with
hydration and the turgidity of the tissues, and through this with
the permeability of the cells and the osmotic concentration of the
tissue fluids. Crozier (1926-1927) has shown the similarity between
the curves for growth and autocatalytic action, and this would seem
to indicate a chemical reaction as a limiting factor in the process,
possibly a reaction resulting in the formation of substances of high
osmotic activity from those of low. Ivanow (1927) has shown that
the position, structure, and mineral and organic content of the petals
indicate the importance of the water relation of this organ.

Bünning (1929) found that the tissues on the two surfaces of the
perianth of *Tulipa gesneriana* behaved differently, protoplasmic activity being directly concerned only on one side. Stern and Bünning
(1929) found temperature the important factor in the daily movements of the leaves of *Phaseolus multiflorus*, changes of one degree
being effective. Daily periodic movements could be displaced by the
reversal of day and night temperature relations.

METHODS

The flowers selected were chosen with a view to obtaining as complete a representation of anthokinetic material as possible. The species used by other investigators in the field were secured when possible, and to these were added many available species that showed movement. It was thus possible to apply the methods of comparative physiology for analysis of the mechanism involved and the effect of the environment upon it. A classified list of the species used is appended to this section.

Field observations were designed to record the behavior of each species, and to compare it with others in the same anthokinetic category under various ecological conditions; to this end cultivated forms were grown and kept under observation in several habitats. Life history studies of each flower were made in the various habitats by means of quantitative methods — the environmental factors of temperature, light, relative humidity and soil moisture being measured periodically, or by means of recording instruments. When analysis of these data showed a correlation between flower behavior and one or more environmental factors, experiments were devised to modify them in the field and to supplement this by determinations of internal conditions and their accompanying variations.

Laboratory work was planned to check the conclusions drawn from field observations and measurements; thus it consisted, first, of the measurement of anthokinetic reactions under carefully controlled conditions designed to approximate those in the field or to modify important ones; second, of the study of the physiological mechanism of the tissues under the various experimental conditions as related to the floral reactions.

Much of the work on flower movement has necessarily been observational; this may be due partly to the difficulty of accurately recording movements in which the degree of curvature differs in the various regions of the moving part. Measurements of the diameter of flowers or of the angle subtended by the perianth must be made at identical points if the results are to be considered comparable. In field work the measurement of angles was found impracticable because of the time required in reading, and the necessity of handling the flowers, thus altering normal conditions. For this work sets of photographs were found to be preferable; by reference to these a record of field behavior could be standardized and field observations made without loss of time.

Although these photographic records served as a guide in the experimental work, the measurement of angles subtended by the perianth tips was employed for these observations. Bristles 1-2 cm.

long were fastened to the perianth tips by means of a gum arabic solution, after the method of Stoppel (1910). The accuracy of the readings was considerably increased by the use of the Smith protractor, and it was found that in many cases the angles could be repeatedly measured with precision at points marked with India ink.

The field behavior was studied at intervals throughout the entire flowering period, during several seasons. Conclusions were checked in some cases by observations under the different conditions of Colorado Springs, Colorado, and Tucson, Arizona. The general flower behavior was first noted in habitats as different as were available for the species. A record of the movements and growth of the bud, the peduncle, and the active portions of the flower was made. By reference to the photographic record the rate of movement was determined and the effect of age and seasonal change evaluated.

Temperature, light, and humidity were measured before and at the time of movement. Since instrumental readings do not show the factors influencing the flower, only approximate values were sought which permitted an understanding of the conditions obtaining at the time of movement. Temperature readings were made by means of thermometers accurate to .2° C., placed with the bulbs within or in close proximity to the flowers. Relative humidity of the air was determined by means of a cog psychrometer. Hygrothermograph records were made in the various habitats with the instruments at approximately the flower level. Light was measured by a stopwatch photometer, using solio paper.

Potometers were made by cutting flowers and also leafy portions of the various species under water and exposing them in weighed and sealed vials of tap water. The seals consisted of plasticine over a cork stopper in which an opening had been cut for the stem. When areas were required they were obtained from blue prints by means of a planimeter. The transpiration of flowers was studied in relation to the opening and closing movements, age, and length of peduncle. The relative water loss of the various flower structures and of the surfaces was checked against the movements by oiling portions of the surface and noting the behavior and loss in weight as compared with unmodified flower potometers, all being exposed in the field at normal levels.

The water content of entire flowers or heads and of those portions most actively concerned in movement was determined by cutting the material desired in the closed, opening, open, and closing stages and placing immediately in weighed vials with rubber stoppers. After weighing to tenths of a milligram, the material was dried to constant weight at 100° C., cooled over calcium chloride, and the loss in weight considered as water.

An attempt was made to determine the relative rate of carbon dioxide evolution in various stages of the movement cycle in the field by passing air at a constant rate through chambers enclosing the flowers and determining the carbon dioxide content. Two constant-flow aspirators, described by Hottes and Hafenrichter (1928), were employed in a battery, one aspirating the flower chamber and the other a blank check. Initial results showed that interpretation of the data in relation to movement was uncertain, due to the effects of changing temperatures and the respiratory activity of the reproductive organs. This work was therefore discontinued.

Although the attempted modification of one factor in the field involved the alteration of several, the results were of value in interpreting flower behavior and in checking the effects of unnatural conditions that necessarily accompany more exact laboratory work. Temperature changes were thus produced in the field by forcing air through a coil of copper tubing heated over a lamp, or cooled by immersion in a mixture of ice and calcium chloride. This method resulted in changing the light and the relative humidity as well as the temperature. For the modification of light in the field, shade-tents were used. Temperature alterations were also produced, but to a degree much less marked than in the heated or cooled bell jars. The absorption of radiant energy was also altered by fixing the flower at abnormal angles, but in no case was this of unquestioned effect, since during the night no result could be expected, and during much of the daylight period a considerable surface reflection from surrounding objects reduced the effectiveness of the method. Wetting the surrounding soil, or reducing the transpiration of the leaves by oiling the surface, was used as a field method for altering the water relations of the plant. The metabolic activities of the flowers were changed by enclosure in chambers containing chloroform vapor or atmospheric air diluted with nitrogen or carbon dioxide.

All flowers under observation were measured and their behavior noted during each daily cycle from the first opening of the bud until the collapse or inactivation of the flower with age. The relation of age to time, rate, and degree of reaction was thus disclosed.

Since much of the laboratory work was carried out with cut flowers, particular care was taken to discover whether cutting changed the normal movements of each species. For this purpose five or more flowers, the history of which was known, were cut under water and exposed in normal position beside undisturbed inflorescences, with water supplied to the cut stems in vials. The observations were designed to determine any change in floral behavior due to cutting, time of cutting, length of peduncle, and exposure of the cut surface to the air. Behavior effects of incipient wilting, partial desiccation, removal

of various floral parts active in opening and closing, and injection of
water into the peduncle or receptacle, were used to obtain additional
field data on the mechanism involved in the various types studied.
For the more accurate control of conditions influencing flower movement, laboratory methods were essential. In this work the following procedure was used.

THE ECOSTAT

An especially designed and constructed apparatus for the control of temperature, light, and humidity was devised, and the term
ecostat (*oikos*, habitat, and *statikos*, stationary) applied.

The ecostat was constructed after the design of similar instruments which have been used so successfully in the laboratory of
plant physiology at the University of Illinois. The authors are
especially indebted to Professor Charles F. Hottes for the use of his
designs and for his constructive suggestions for the modifications
required. The authors are also indebted to the Johnson Service Company of Milwaukee, Wisconsin, for their interest and cooperation.

The entire apparatus as used is shown in Plate 1, and a cross-
section drawing to give the essential features of construction in Figure
1. The ecostat is designed to give delicate, accurate, automatic and
independent control of temperature, humidity, and light. In order
to reproduce field conditions, it is constructed to control each factor
over a wide range — temperature, for example, between 10° and 50°
C. — and to allow a change from one set of conditions to another in a
very short time. The size, weight, and construction of the instrument are such that it can be transported easily and without danger
to the delicate controls.

The ecostat consists of two separate, independent, glass-enclosed
chambers mounted on a common base and covered with light-tight
reflecting hoods. Each chamber has an outside cubic dimension of
24 inches, giving an internal volume of 9250 cubic inches, and is
equipped with a thermostat, humidostat, light filter, and instruments
for measuring and recording temperature, humidity, and light. The
base of the apparatus is 75 x 25 x 17 inches, constructed of white pine,
and divided into three chambers, each of which has an internal dimension of 23 x 23 x 16 inches. The central chamber houses the
switch board, compressed air controls, and humidifiers. The two
outer chambers contain the cooling coils, brine tanks, heating coils,
and the air-circulating mechanism with its automatic controls, and
lie immediately below the experimental chambers. The cooling coil
and brine tank are separated from the rest of the apparatus in each
chamber by an air-tight partition heavily insulated with celotex,
as shown in Figure 1.

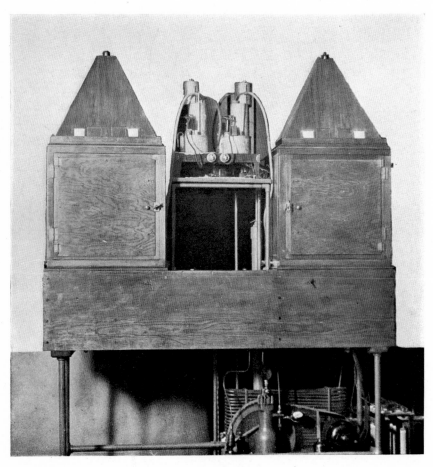

The Ecostat

The entire apparatus is supported at suitable height on a framework of iron pipe which allows adjustment for leveling the apparatus

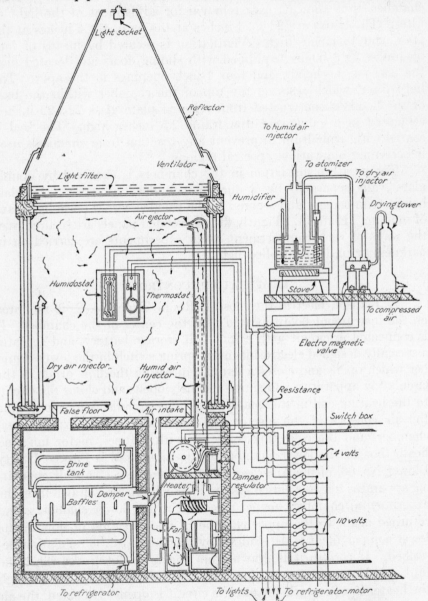

FIG. 1.—An ecostat chamber and the connected control mechanism.

and also houses the electric refrigeration unit which is mounted on a cushioning suspension (Plate 1).

The reflecting hood above each chamber is made of heavy galvanized iron, enameled white on the inside to insure the maximum efficiency from the lights installed in the top. It is mounted on a wooden base which fits inside a retaining molding on the top of the chamber, thus allowing easy removal for adjustment of the light or filter. The hoods are 23 x 23 inches at the base, 4 x 4 inches at the apex, and 18 inches high. Ventilation is secured by means of four openings, 3 x 3 inches, equipped with sliding doors and located near the base of the hoods, and four 1-inch openings in the apex. The light filter, which rests on the top of the chamber within the base of the hood, is constructed from selected plate glass 22 x 22 inches, cemented in a galvanized iron frame 2.5 inches high. The seal is coated with asphaltum to prevent any reaction from chemicals used in screening out various spectral regions.

Temperature insulation in the chambers is obtained by double glass walls separated by a quarter-inch dead air space, the glass being set in cement and secured to the wooden corner posts by means of molding (Plate 1). Tightly fitting wooden panels are secured over the walls of each compartment when experiments are carried on in darkness or under controlled light.

TEMPERATURE CONTROL

A Johnson electric thermostat, Room Type No. 2, is mounted on the instrument board located near the center of the chamber. It is connected in circuit with a four-volt storage battery, and actuates a specially designed electro-magnetic spring switch in the lower chamber which opens and closes a damper directing the flow of air in the circulating apparatus, and simultaneously opens and closes the circuit to the heating coil in the heater box. The apparatus for circulating the air consists of the ejector and false floor in the experimental chamber, and the collecting conveyor with damper, motor fan, and heater box in the lower chamber. The motor fan is Sirocco Utility Blower No. 00, of the American Blower Company. This air-circulating apparatus makes a closed system in which the air is drawn from the experimental chamber, heated or cooled in the lower chambers, and returned again to the upper chamber. The direction of flow in the lower compartment is determined by the thermostatic regulation described. If cooled, it is drawn from the false floor, over the brine tank into the conveyor and fan, and delivered to the ejector through the heater box in which the electric circuit is open. If heated, the air is drawn directly from the false floor into the conveyor fan, and passes through the heater box to which the circuit is closed, and into the ejector. In Figure 1 the flow of air is shown directed over the heating coil. The purpose of the ejector and false floor is the even distribution of the air in the chambers. This closed system of circulation requires heating or cooling the air in the chambers but one or two degrees, and hence allows accurate control. Thermograph records show that the temperature of the air in the chamber seldom varies more than .5° from that desired by the operator. The selection of a thermo-regulation system operating on a double circuit not only increases the accuracy of control, but allows a wide range of temperature selection. The type of thermostat used can be adjusted very closely and requires a minimum of attention when in operation.

The cooling system consists of a brine tank containing calcium chloride solution, for each compartment. The surface area of each tank is 500 square inches, but this is greatly increased by a system of baffles. The tanks are cooled by coils and a single compressor unit of the Universal Refrigeration Company, using methyl chloride. This unit has its own thermo-regulator which is set by the operator according to the temperature desired in the experimental chambers. Although methyl chloride was selected in preference to other gases used in electric refrigeration, because the escape of imperceptible amounts would exert a minimum toxicity on the plants, nevertheless the utmost care was used in setting up the unit to prevent leakage. Even in case of leakage the escaping gas could hardly reach the experimental chambers, because of the remoteness of the condenser pump and the submergence of the expansion coils in the brine. Since the apparatus for circulating air is a closed system, the danger of gases from the room entering the experimental chambers is minimized.

HUMIDITY CONTROL

The relative humidity is controlled by the injection of moist or dry air into the experimental chambers. This in turn is regulated by a Johnson humidostat on the instrument board in the chamber, and connected in series with a four-volt battery circuit and a Johnson electro-magnetic I. P. air-valve which receives compressed air maintained at a pressure of 20 pounds per square inch. The valve directs the air through a specially constructed humidifier, or through a calcium chloride drying tower, and into the chambers according to the contacts made by the humidostat. In Figure 1 the drying tower is shown connected directly in the compressed air line.

The humidifier consists of a galvanized iron container mounted on an electric heating unit, and enclosing an atomizer of large capacity which when receiving air through the electro-magnetic valve humidifies the air in the container and forces it into the chambers. Because of the necessity for accurate temperature control, it is undesirable to introduce into the experimental chamber a stream of air the temperature of which differs widely from the desired range. The water in the humidifier may be heated and any desired temperature maintained by means of a three-ampere heating unit beneath, controlled by a DeKhotinsky thermo-regulator. Cooling devices for the humidifier were found unnecessary, because at low temperatures very little moisture is required in the experimental chambers. The humidifier is also provided with a constant level device of common design (not shown in Figure 1) for maintaining the proper volume of water.

This system of humidity control will maintain the relative humidity of the air in the experimental chambers within a range of 25 to 75 per cent, at all temperatures within the capacity of the ecostat, with a maximum variation of 5 per cent. At humidities greater than 75 per cent, the limits of control are slightly greater.

LIGHT CONTROL

Light is supplied the compartments by Edison Mazda nitrogen-filled bulbs mounted at the apex of the hood. The desired intensity is obtained by using bulbs of different current consumption, the light filter, and in case of very low intensity, by inserting a resistance of proper size in series with the lamp. The use of water in the light filter provides thermal insulation by screening out the longer waves, and various solutions may be used for the absorption of different spectral regions. In all cases the quality and quantity of light reaching the plant in the experimental chamber must be measured by standardized illuminometer and spectroscope.

LABORATORY PROCEDURE

Ecostat studies were designed first to test the behavior of flower types under conditions of constant temperature, light, and relative humidity. The periodic reactions were compared in time and rate with field checks, and the comparative behavior was studied in this manner at various levels of temperature, light, and humidity. As the three controlled factors were changed singly, any reaction was recorded by angle measurements made at intervals of one hour or less, according to the speed of movement. Changes were usually made at the normal time for the expected and the reverse movements, and at intermediate times as behavior required to determine the periodicity curve. Temperatures from 10° to 40° were used, light values ranged from 0 to 500 candle meters, and relative humidities from 20 to 95 per cent saturation. The attempt was made to determine the magnitude of change in a single factor necessary to cause an opening or closing reaction, and the relation of this to time of day, level of other factors, habitat conditions, season, age, time of cutting, and length of periods since the preceding stimulation and reaction.

In so limited a region as that actively concerned in flower movement, micro-methods alone can furnish direct measurements, but for this a better technique than has yet been developed is greatly to be desired. A detailed microscopic examination of freshly cut sections of active tissue was made under suitable magnifications. Sections of active tissue and of epidermis, stripped from the regions concerned, were plasmolyzed with solutions of sucrose. Tissues were taken from flowers in various stages of opening and closing in the field, as well as from those in the ecostat chambers, with the object of obtaining comparative results from the opposing sides of the active organs. Sections from opposing surfaces were mounted simultaneously in the same solution and frequently under a single cover glass. Sections were placed immediately in the solution to be tested so that no changes either in the concentration of the solution or the permeability of the section occurred from previous use. Sections were observed after 20 minutes in the solution at approximately 20° C., the time and temperature being kept constant during comparative observations. The sucrose solutions used were freshly made up from chemically pure material and the values checked frequently by means of the Abbé refractometer. The solutions were made up with differences no greater than .1 molar when the approximate concentration of the tissue fluid was known. A solution was considered slightly hypertonic when the majority of the cells to be seen in three high-power fields showed the beginning of plasmolytic contraction in 10 minutes at 20°.

Some determinations of suction force were made by measuring the cells to ascertain the initial contraction, but this method was discontinued since it seemed to give results similar to those of plasmolysis and also had the disadvantage of greatly reducing the number of cells observed. Attempts to estimate the hydrophilic colloids of the tissue by staining with malachite green were not successful because of the difficulty of measuring the dye absorption by micromethods. An apparatus for determining the freezing point of the cell sap under the microscope was developed and employed to a limited extent in checking plasmolytic results. The temperature of an insulated microscope stage was controlled by the circulation of a calcium chloride solution heated by an electric resistance coil or cooled by carbon dioxide expansion. The mount was enclosed between an upper and lower compartment, and the temperatures obtained by means of a thermocouple, while the formation of ice crystals was observed under dark-field illumination. As most of the present work had been completed before the micro-cryoscope was available, little progress was made in this promising line, but this work is being continued.

SPECIES STUDIED

The following species were studied in more or less detail, but experimental work was limited to a few representatives of different types.

HEMERANTHOUS

Acroclinium roseum
Agoseris californica
Agoseris grandiflora
Agoseris major
Ammobium alatum
Anagallis arvensis
Anagallis grandiflora
Arctotis grandis
Aster bigelovi
Calochortus gunnisoni
Cichorium intybus
Crepis alpina
Crepis foetida
Crepis runcinata
Crepis tectorum
Dimorphotheca aurantiaca
Eschscholtzia californica
Gentiana amarella
Gentiana calycosa
Gentiana frigida
Gilia aurea
Gilia capitata
Gilia densiflora
Gilia tricolor
Glaucium corniculatum
Godetia grandiflora

Helichrysum bracteatum
Hieracium boreale
Hieracium sabaudum
Hieracium saxifragum
Lactuca pulchella
Layia elegans
Linum rubrum grandiflorum
Malacothrix californica
Malacothrix fendleri
Malva moschata
Malva rotundifolia
Mentzelia lindleyi
Papaver argemone
Papaver dubium
Papaver hybridum
Ptiloria tenuifolia
Reichardia tingitana
Rosa woodsi
Sonchus arvensis
Sphaeralcea coulteri
Taraxacum officinale
Tolpis barbata
Tragopogon porrifolius
Tragopogon pratensis
Tulipa gesneriana
Xeranthemum annuum

EPHEMERAL-HEMERANTHOUS

Convolvulus arvensis
Convolvulus elongatus
Convolvulus major
Convolvulus repens
Convolvulus sepium
Convolvulus tricolor
Echinocactus galeotti
Erodium cicutarium
Hibiscus trionum

Ipomoea leptophylla
Ipomoea purpurea
Ipomoea rubro-coerulea
Ipomoea setosa
Linum usitatissimum
Linum perenne
Portulaca oleracea
Tradescantia virginiana
Tribulus terrestris

NYCTANTHOUS

Mentzelia multiflora   *Mentzelia nuda*

EPHEMERAL-NYCTANTHOUS

Agrostemma githago   *Oenothera coronopifolia*
Allionia nyctaginea   *Oenothera drummondi*
Gaura coccinea   *Oenothera hookeri*
Gaura parviflora   *Oenothera lamarckiana*
Godetia quadrivulnera   *Oenothera missouriensis*
Ipomoea grandiflora   *Oenothera pallida*
Mirabilis jalapa   *Oenothera rhombipetala*
Mirabilis longiflora   *Oenothera rosea*
Oenothera albicaulis   *Oenothera spiralis*
Oenothera biennis   *Oenothera trichocalyx*
Oenothera bistorta   *Silene inflata*
Oenothera caespitosa   *Silene noctiflora*

II

TULIPA GESNERIANA

FIELD BEHAVIOR

The varieties of *Tulipa gesneriana* differ more in floral shape and color and in the flowering season than in field behavior. The Cottage and Darwin varieties were used for this work. At Colorado Springs during May and June the large erect buds opened by 8 A.M., remained open throughout the day, and closed at or shortly after sundown, 6 to 7 P.M. During cool days in the early part of the flowering season the flowers open later in the morning and may close by noon. During late June, flowers fully exposed to sun and wind closed before noon in a slightly flaccid condition.

The rate of movement in the field was variable, being influenced by several independent factors such as temperature, season, and age of flower. Observations on ten flowers opening for the second time in the field at Colorado Springs in May gave an average of 32 minutes for the opening and 67 for the closing movement. June readings gave lower values, but the difference was slight because the degree of maximum expansion of flowers of equal age increased with the lateness of the season.

As the flowers became older, the perianth parts opened to a greater angle in the morning and failed to close completely at night. The daily movements were repeated until the flower withered, its age at this time depending on weather conditions. During the early part of the flowering season, flowers may remain active for 8 days, but if exposed to high temperatures and wind, two days often marks the extent of active life. The severity of conditions promoting rapid desiccation seemed to control the active life of the flower.

STRUCTURE

The basal thickening of the perianth parts of the tulip has been recognized as a pulvinus since the work of Pfeffer. This structure is largely composed of parenchymatous tissue, with the cells so arranged that movement can take place without a shearing action (Farmer, 1902), and are abundantly supplied with intercellular spaces into which cell fluids may escape with a consequent reduction of turgidity. The outer epidermis is more heavily cuticularized than the inner. Stomata are absent or functionless. Although a portion of the curvature occurs over the entire perianth, by far the greater amount

30

takes place in the region of the basal thickening which thus is of especial importance.

MEASUREMENT OF FACTORS IN THE FIELD

Air temperature, relative humidity, light, and evaporation were measured in close proximity to the flowers of *Tulipa gesneriana* under observation. Only general quantitative relations could be discovered. While the flowers opened under increasing temperature, light, and evaporation rate, and closed under reverse relations, the records did not show a positive correlation between the reaction time, or the rate of movement, and the intensity of the factors operative at the time.

Transpiration observed in ten flowers at Colorado Springs, June 6, gave the following results, computed on the area determined from the blue prints of the flower parts made at the close of the experiment, and expressed in grams loss per hour per square centimeter of perianth surface. Evaporation was measured from a small blackened pan exposed at flower level six feet away.

Time	Condition of Flowers	Transpiration	Evaporation	Transpiration-Evaporation
5–6 a.m.	Closed	0.020	0.006	3.3
6–7	Opening	0.018	0.007	2.6
7–9	Open	0.026	0.007	3.7
9–11	....	0.035	0.009	3.9
11–1 p.m.	....	0.042	0.010	4.2
1–3	....	0.048	0.010	4.8
3–5	....	0.046	0.014	3.3
5–6	....	0.037	0.013	2.8
6–7	....	0.024	0.008	3.0
7–9	Closed	0.025	0.007	3.6

There is no evidence here, or in similar determinations of which this is typical, of an altered transpiration rate ascribable to the position of the flower parts. This is perhaps due to errors unavoidable in the method of measurement. Since transpiration in the tulip flower is largely cuticular, the fall in relative transpiration-evaporation rate in the afternoon is probably caused by the partial desiccation of the tissues. To check this, the water content of the basal portion of the perianth parts was determined at intervals during, immediately preceding, and following the opening and closing of the flower. For this purpose, only flowers were used which were known to have opened for the first time on the same day as those used in the transpiration study given above. Results are expressed in percentage water of original weight.

Time	5:30 a.m.	6:15 a.m.	5:45 p.m.	6:30 p.m.	9 p.m.
Water Content %	96.24	96.28	90.65	90.57	91.35

These results show that in the basal portion of tulip perianth the water content of the tissue is high immediately preceding and at the time of opening of the flower, and falls to a lower level at the time of closing.

FIELD EXPERIMENTS

A number of experiments designed to control the factors in the field were undertaken. For reasons already discussed, the results from such work can only be utilized in a very general way, but they afford a check against any possible effects caused by abnormal conditions incident to the more detailed laboratory experiments. The following is typical of results obtained in several similar experiments.

May 20, at 8:15 A.M. four tulip flowers were covered with two bell jars, the flowers being in the shade at an air temperature of 9° C., and a relative humidity of 51 per cent. The temperature of the first or control jar varied between 9° and 9.2° during the experiment; the humidity rose to 60 per cent. Heated air was forced into the second bell jar at the rate of 100 cc. per second, the temperature rising as follows: 8:15, 9°; 8:30, 16°; 8:45, 19°; 9, 19.5°. During this time the relative humidity rose to 63 per cent. One flower in the second bell jar began to open at 8:25 and was fully expanded at 8:50; the second flower responded similarly, 8:45 to 9. During this experimental period the checks enclosed within the control jar did not open, and this was also true of the untreated flowers in the adjacent bed.

At 11:50 A.M. five flowers were cut under water, all being fully open for the third successive day. One of these flowers was supplied with a vial of water and left in the bed at normal exposure, two were similarly placed and covered with a light-tight box, and the remaining two were placed in darkness in a refrigerator at 2.3°. The temperature in the dark box was variable but averaged 18.8° for the experimental period. Humidity values both in the dark box and the refrigerator approached saturation; in the open bed the readings ranged between 40 and 50 per cent. The flowers in the refrigerator closed in 45 minutes, while those in the dark box and those at normal exposure in the bed remained open.

Field results such as these confirm the conclusions of Pfeffer and of numerous later workers that tulip flowers respond in their opening and closing movements mainly to temperature changes.

Flowers cut under water were repeatedly exposed in the bed adjacent to normal uncut flowers of the same age and variety, but in no case did any abnormal behavior result from cutting within 48 hours. The exposure of cut flowers unprovided with a supply of water resulted in closure with the progress of tissue desiccation.

LABORATORY EXPERIMENTS

Several colors of the Cottage and Darwin varieties of *Tulipa gesneriana* were grown in garden beds at Baldwin, Kansas. The bulbs were planted in free soil, or in 3-inch pots embedded in the soil. The plants flowered throughout April, the flowers opening from 8 to 11 A.M., and closing by 4 P.M., or on cool days remaining closed.

Cut flowers were used, since cutting did not change the floral behavior, while the removal of potted plants from the soil disturbed the root systems and resulted in a lag in the temperature and humidity control of the ecostat chambers. All flowers used were cut under water and immediately placed in the chambers of the ecostat, which was in operation in the nearby laboratory kindly supplied for this purpose by Baker University. In all cases the unopened buds were tagged in the field and a history of their behavior for several days recorded to make sure that all material used in an experiment was of equal active age. Uncut flowers comparable to those used in the experimental chambers were left in the bed for reference as to field behavior. Similar flowers were cut and left in the bed at normal exposure and supplied with the same tap-water furnished the flowers under experiment.

The degree of opening was measured with the protractor at the outset of the experiment and at succeeding intervals, without opening the chambers or disturbing conditions within. The values tabulated are computed from these readings in percentage of full opening, based on the average maximum expansion observed in the set.

In this connection the flowers were placed in the field at the close of the experiments and the maximum expansion recorded and compared with that found both before cutting and in the ecostat. The values given in Table 1 are thus comparisons with the maximum movement of which the flowers used were capable. The post-experimental field behavior in all cases showed an approximately normal reaction to field conditions. The experimental conditions were thus not so abnormal or prolonged so greatly as to change the behavior of the flowers, and the responses obtained may be recorded with considerable surety as normal.

PERIODICITY

In order to determine any periodic movements present, tulip flowers were studied under conditions of various constant temperatures, light, and humidity. All flowers were cut immediately before

the beginning of the experiments. Readings at the compared temperatures are given in similarly numbered columns, right and left,
in Table 1. Each value is averaged from the readings made on ten
flowers.

From the results of Experiment 1 and the curves of these values
shown in Figure 2, it will be seen that a closing reaction occurred
at the beginning of the experiment and was followed by a gradual
expansion to approximately complete opening which persisted until
the end of the experiment. The slight unavoidable cooling of the
flowers as they were brought from the bed through the laboratory
to the ecostat accounts for the initial closing movement, since this
result did not follow cutting when the flowers were left in the field.
This initial closing movement continued two hours after the intro-
duction of the flowers into the experimental chambers, and the rapid
ensuing expansion carried the opening to a point from which the
rate fell to the curve of gradual expansion characteristic of the second
period of activity. The opening process, occurring during the afternoon, was slow and only reached completion during the morning
hours of the following day. No periodic movement was shown.

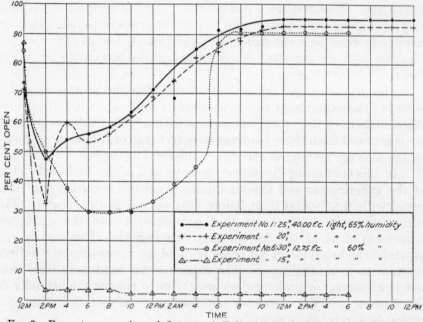

Fig. 2.—Percentage opening of flowers of *Tulipa gesneriana* under constant conditions at different temperature levels.

For the further study of periodic movement and of the temperature relations of the flowers, an extended series of experiments was
carried out under various constant conditions as well as with controlled variations.

TABLE 1

TULIPA GESNERIANA

Behavior (per cent open) of flowers subjected to various constant temperatures at different times of day. Ex. 1: 40 foot-candles, 65% humidity, 25° and 20° C. Ex. 8: flowers changed reciprocally between 30° and 15° C. Ex. 2-7: 12.75 foot-candles, 60% humidity, 30° and 15° C. Readings at 15° are marked with an asterisk.

1	2	3	4	5	6	7	8	Experiment No. / Time	1	2	3	4	5	6	7	8
	4.2							2 a.m.		2.4						
	16.9							4		2.4						
	42.6							6		2.4	8.2					
	49.8							8		2.4	17.7	2.4				
	40.3			87.9				10		2.4	17.7	2.4	85.9			
73	40.3	8.7	2.3	96.2	84.2			12 m.	70.9	2.4	10.6	0	23.7	87.0		
47.4	40.3	54.5	39.1	75.9	50.0	58.0	44.7	2 p.m.	32.6	2.4	2.4	0	18.9	3.5	37.9	49.1*
54.0	35.6	55.7	47.4	60.4	37.9	22.4	46.6	4	59.8	2.4	2.4	0	18.9	3.5	15.4	7.1*
55.6	33.2	35.5	42.6	60.4	29.6	20.1	45.6	6	53.3	0	2.4	0	14.2	3.5	10.0	8.3*
58.6	37.9	34.3	47.4	52.1	29.6	18.7	11.8*	8	56.2	0	2.4	0	14.2	3.5	3.6	14.4
63.2	37.9	30.8	42.6	59.3	33.2	23.0	11.8*	10	61.9	0	2.4	0	14.2	2.3	2.4	25.4
70.1	37.9	30.8	32.3	79.2	39.0	25.3	11.8*	12 mt.	68.2	0	2.4	0	14.2	2.3	2.4	25.4
67.9	37.9	26.0	32.3	89.1	45.0	31.1	11.8*	2 a.m.	74.0	0	2.4	0	14.2	2.3	2.4	25.4
85.1	37.9	23.7	32.3	100	86.7	70.6	11.8*	4	81.8	0	2.4	0	23.7	2.3	2.4	50.1
91.1	42.6	23.7	32.3	100	90.2	85.7	100	6	84.1	9.5	2.4	0	23.7	2.3	2.4	37.7*
91.6	47.5	23.7	32.3	100	90.2	87.8	26.1*	8	87.6	9.5	2.4	0	23.7	2.3	2.4	35.2*
92.3	47.5	27.2	35.6	100	90.2	89.6	16.6*	10	91.2	9.5	2.4	0	23.7	2.3	2.4	33.7*
94.8	47.5	27.2	36.7	100	90.2	90.5	73.5	12 m.	92.4	9.5	2.4	0	26	2.3	2.4	32.5*
94.8	47.5	35.5	39.1	100	90.2	91.3	100	2 p.m.	92.4	9.5	2.4	0	26	2.3	2.4	32.5
94.8	47.5	35.5	39.1	100	90.2	91	11.8*	4	92.4	9.5	2.4	0	26	2.3	2.4	40.3
94.8	47.5	33.1	40.3	100	90.2	91.1	11.0*	6	92.4	9.5	2.4	0	26	2.3	2.4	46.1
94.8	47.5	33.1	41.5	100		91.1	10.4*	8	92.4	9.5	2.4				2.4	45.2
94.8	47.5	33.1	41.5	100			10.2*	10	92.4	9.5						13.1*
94.8	47.5	33.1	41.5	100				12 mt.	92.4	9.5						

In Experiment 2, the average results of which are graphed in Figure 3, the flowers were installed at 2 A.M. when in the closed condition. Both the 30° and 15° curves show periodic movement during the first daylight period, closing slightly in the afternoon, remaining constant through the night, and reopening the following morning. No evidence of this periodicity appeared after the opening of the second day, during which the flowers maintained a position proportional to the temperature.

Experiment 3 differed from Experiment 2 in that the flowers were placed under experimental conditions at 6 A.M. The 30° curve agrees in general with that of Experiment 2, showing a slight periodic opening and closing in the forenoon and afternoon respectively of the first day. At 15°, after an initial opening movement due to brief exposure to the laboratory temperature which was considerably above that of the bed at this time of day, the flowers closed and exhibited no periodic movement.

When Experiment 4 was begun at about the normal opening time, 8 A.M., a similar result was obtained, as may be seen from the curves shown in Figure 3. These curves differ from the corresponding ones in Experiments 2 and 3 chiefly in displaying an increased rate of reaction, and a longer and more nearly normal open period at 30°. Periodic movements are shown as before in the slight closing in the afternoon, and reopening the following morning. At 15°, the flowers closed in four hours and exhibited no further periodic movement. In this case again, periodic effects were absent.

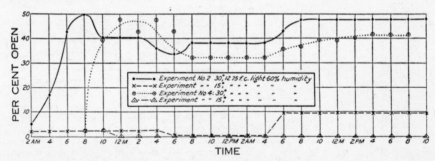

Fig 3.—Percentage opening of flowers of *Tulipa gesneriana* under constant conditions at different temperature levels.

At 10 A.M. the flowers had just previously reached full expansion. In Experiment 5 (Fig. 4), when they were placed in the chambers, closure began immediately at 15°, and after but 2 hours at 30°. The periodic movements, while conspicuous, were hastened so that both the closing and the succeeding opening began before the usual normal daily period.

Experiment 6 (Fig. 2), like Experiment 1, was started at noon. Rapid closing was followed by the periodic morning opening only in the 30° chamber.

In Experiment 7 (Fig. 4) flowers which were closing were used. After completing the closing movement they remained closed at 15°, but soon began the opening process at 30°, and continued a gradual expansion which persisted almost to the close of the experiment. No purely periodic movements were evident.

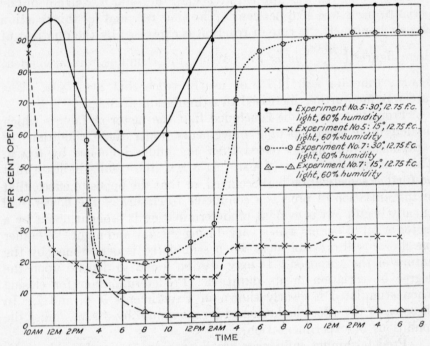

Fig. 4.—Percentage opening of flowers of *Tulipa gesneriana* under constant conditions at different temperature levels.

It is evident from the results of these experiments that daily periodic movements are frequently shown by tulip flowers under the experimental conditions here used, at 30° C. This movement appeared only during the first daily period after removal from the field, and displayed the greatest amplitude in flowers which were exposed to field conditions during the morning and were removed to the experimental chambers in the open condition. It appears that this periodicity is predetermined by the exposure of the flower to daytime field conditions, and that in the absence of additional external stimuli of this nature the intensity of the periodic movement falls rapidly in four to six hours. Periodic movements were largely suppressed at 15°, and did not appear in flowers placed at noon under an illumination of 40 foot-candles and at 20° or 25° temperature. At 15° there was a more or less permanent closure, while at higher temperatures and intense illumination there was a gradual and lasting expansion, indicating a stimulating effect which masked the periodic one.

The rate of reaction of tulip flowers in response to temperature stimuli is predetermined. This effect is evident when the temperature stimuli are applied at different times of day and night. When a stimulus of 30° C. was applied at 2 A.M., the total movement of the perianth parts was 45.6 per cent. The time required for this reaction was six hours. If the rate of reaction is expressed by the quotient of these figures $\left(\dfrac{45.6}{6}\right)$ it is 7.6. When the stimulus was applied at 6 A.M., the rate was 11.75, or nearly twice that at 2 A.M. The rate was not further increased by stimulation at 8 A.M.

From this it may be concluded that the factor or factors which predetermine floral opening movements under these conditions of experimentation have exerted their maximum influence by 6 A.M. This was not the case at 2 A.M. At 8 A.M. the results indicate that no further sensitization had occurred, or that the opposite effect, that of the initiation of processes conducive to closure of the flower, had already begun. It is evident predetermination is brought about by a factor or set of factors which vary during the day and night. Whether the flower will open or close when stimulated is determined by the nature of the variation. It may also be found to depend upon the degree of variation or its duration. Predetermination for closing when stimulated is clearly shown in Experiments 5, 6, and 7. In these cases the effect had reached its maximum by 3 P.M., under the conditions of experimentation.

Predetermining influences are even more noticeable when the rate of reaction analysis is applied to the second opening movement in Experiments 2 to 7 inclusive. The ability of the flowers to react by opening a second time seems to depend largely upon an induced rhythm previously but recently set in motion. The rhythm apparently depends upon conditions in the field during the forenoon hours. This becomes evident when the rates of reaction in Experiments 2, 3, and 4 are compared with the rates in Experiments 5, 6, and 7. In the former, predetermining conditions were not active, while in the latter they were in play. This predetermined sensitization is apparently conditioned by a critical period. In Experiments 6 and 7 the opening reaction, though of greater magnitude, was delayed several hours. It may be assumed that a counteracting or inhibiting influence is at play in the field during the two hours immediately preceding noon.

That light intensity rather than temperature is likely to be the predominating factor in predetermination effects may be concluded by comparing Experiments 1 and 6. This is further emphasized in Experiments 9 and 10.

The closing rates at 15° for 2, 6, 8, and 10 A.M., 12 noon, and 3 P.M. are .15, 1.94, .6, 8.97, 8.47, and 5.05, respectively. In the closing movement there is thus a periodicity, with a predetermined critical period in the later forenoon on both sides of which the closing rate decreases.

In Experiment 8, sets of flowers were interchanged between the chambers at various times to check the results of temperature variations, and to ascertain the effects of periodicity when tending toward or against the stimulated response. In selecting the sets for the experimental chambers, care was exercised to obtain flowers of the same variety and age. The results show very clearly the effects of periodicity. From 3 to 6 P.M., the 15° set closed rapidly, while those at 30° remained almost motionless. At 6 P.M., when the conditions were reversed, rapid closure followed exposure of the partly open flowers in the 15° chamber, while the set of closed flowers from the 15° chamber expanded very slightly at 30° until after 2 A.M. The flowers that remained closed in the 15° chamber during the night hours expanded to full opening immediately when transferred at 4 A.M. to the 30° chamber. At 15°, closure followed in 4 hours, and the reopening was completed in an equal time when the flowers were placed in the 30° chamber at 10 A.M. The subjection of this set to 15° at 2 P.M. resulted in rapid closing. The reciprocal set of flowers which had been held at 30° during the night hours and 15° during the day, never greatly exceeded 50 per cent expansion after 10 hours in conditions which when applied in the morning resulted in complete opening in two hours. It is noteworthy that where exposure to a temperature of 30° resulted in complete opening, the process was more rapid when initiated at 6 A.M. than at 10 A.M. At the same time the closing process initiated by a temperature of 15° was less rapid when begun at 6 A.M. than at 2 P.M.

Tulip flowers often show periodic movements under conditions of constant temperature, light, and humidity, tending to produce opening in the morning and closing in the afternoon. Since under constant conditions these movements persist but for one day after removal from the field, they are doubtless predetermined by the periodic cycle of factors during the preceding day. These periodic movements are largely inhibited by a temperature of 15°, and may be masked by the exposure of the flowers to an illumination of 40 foot-candles intensity. Periodicity is also shown by variations in response to thermal stimuli of constant intensity which result in responses of maximum amplitude when the movement agrees with the periodic tendency effective at the time, and minimum amplitude when the stimulated and periodic movements are opposed.

EFFECTS OF TEMPERATURE

Experiments 1 to 8 inclusive show that under similar conditions of treatment, age, and variety, the degree of expansion of tulip flowers varied with the temperature to which they were subjected between 15° and 30°. While the flowers responded to temperature changes by opening under increased temperature and closing under decreased temperature within this range, the response differed in amplitude, depending on the direction of the daily periodic movement which would normally occur at or near the time of stimulation. The effect of different temperature levels was well shown in Experiment 1, where the curve (Fig. 2) for 25° maintains a level above that for 20°. There was no significant difference between the rates or time of initiation of the reaction, the latent period being two hours in both cases; but there was a general difference in the level of the curves, corresponding to the temperature. (Latent period has been used heretofore to indicate the duration of stimulation; our use is the more logical one of the period of inactivity between the application of a stimulus of any intensity and the response to it). If the maximum and minimum openings, which are attained only when the movement is favored by periodicity, are averaged, we have at temperatures 15°, 20°, 25°, and 30° C, the maximum angular openings of 19°, 150°, 152°, and 180°, and the minimum of −35°. The entire maximum angular movement of the perianth is thus 54°, 185°, 187°, and 215° for the above temperatures. It is obvious that for the first 20 hours, or until the final equilibrium value is reached, a comparison of temperature effects must be made only at equivalent times.

When the flowers have received different treatment previous to the experiment, a comparison of the absolute values of the results is not possible. Thus the maximum to which the flowers opened in Experiments 2, 3, and 4 is far less than the values to be expected at this temperature from the results shown in Experiments 5, 6, and 7. Experiment 8 shows that when sudden temperature changes between 15° and 30° are such that the resulting movement agrees in direction with the periodic tendency, complete opening or closing is produced under constant light and humidity conditions.

EFFECTS OF LIGHT

The average results of four typical experiments carried out under variations of light are given in Table 2. Ten flowers of *Tulipa gesneriana* were used in each experiment, and all material was handled as already described in connection with the experiments on temperature effects. The ecostat chambers were maintained at 25° and 60 per cent humidity, and the light changes were made between darkness and an intensity of 40 foot-candles by switching the lights off and on without disturbing the flowers in any way. The readings made in darkness are marked with an asterisk. Comparative readings from sets given reciprocal light and dark periods are shown in similarly numbered columns right and left in Table 2.

TABLE 2
TULIPA GESNERIANA

Behavior (percentage open) of flowers subjected to constant conditions of 25°C. and 60% relative humidity, and to darkness or to 40 foot-candles light intensity, at various times of day.

Readings in darkness are marked with an asterisk.

Experiment No.	9	10	11	12	9	10	11	12
Time								
1 a.m.	2.6				6.1*			
2	38.7				4.3*			
4	41.9				15.9*			
6	58.1	0*			30*	0.8		
8	59.8	21.0*			30*	26.4		
10	62.2	41.4*			32.4*	59.1		
12 m.	77.1	28.4*	39.5		45*	40.8	38.9*	
2 p.m.	71.0*	26.1	22.9		48.1	24.5*	20.6*	
4	70.1*	26.9	43.1		52.9	22.1*	23.2*	
6	63.3*	26.1	52.9	5.5	64	18.9*	29.2*	2.4
8	60.5*	25.4	50.1	5.5	62.1	21.3*	30.8*	5.3
10	60.5*	29.2	58.0	7.1	62.8	18.2*	36*	9.5
12 mt.	52.0*	40.3	65.6	7.1	64.4	33.2*	38.6*	10.6
2 a.m.	70.3	37.8*	67.9*	9.6	46.6*	36.3	54.9	13*
4	92.6	35.5*	79.9*	12.2	49.8*	39.7	68.7	15.4*
6	90.6	33.6*	82.3*	15.6	43.5*	45	66.2	20.1*
8	89.8	37.9*	82.3	14.8	42.6*	48.2	56.8*	29.5*
10	88.5	37.1*	100	26.5	43.5*	45.8	65.5*	36.7*
12 m.	91.1	40.2*	100	34	48*	45	76*	49.6*
2 p.m.	89.3*	61.5	100*	25.2*	79.3	35.3*	67.7	59.2
4	84.2*	54.4	100*	20.1*	80.3	25.5*	61	76.9
6	65.5*	48.2	100*	20.9*	82.1	32.3*	63.3	75.9
8	70.3*	57.7		10.7*	82.9	34.8*		79.5
10	73.3*	22.3		7.1*	81.9	34.8*		87.9
12 mt.	74.7*	47.3		6.5*	80.9	34.8*		89.1
2 a.m.				15.4				91.1
4				24.8				92.2
6				30.8				96.2
8				32				96.2
10				37.9				100
12 m.				64.2				100

When Experiment 9 was started at 1 A.M. the illuminated flowers, in response to the periodic opening of the morning, expanded to a greater degree than those in darkness. When the lighting was reversed at noon, a closing movement of low rate followed the change into darkness, while the periodic opening evident in the darkened set during the morning hours was slowly carried to a higher level during the afternoon. On reversing the illumination at midnight a rapid opening to full expansion followed lighting. Darkening at midnight produced closing, followed by partial opening before noon. The second light change at noon was followed by slow closing in the darkness and slight opening in the light. These results show a stimulating effect for light of 40 foot-candles intensity, and that it is largely effective in producing flower movements when agreeing in direction with periodic movements. After the first day the flowers for which the light period was the reverse of the usual daily cycle showed displaced periodicity, going through slight closing movements in response to darkening during the morning, and partial opening in response to light in the afternoon.

The curves for the average results of Experiments 9 and 10 are shown in Figure 5.

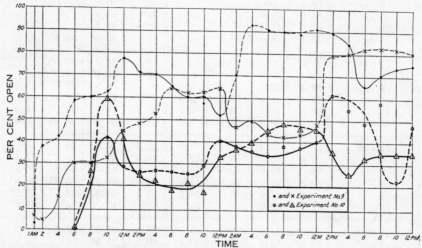

Fig. 5.—Percentage opening of flowers of *Tulipa gesneriana* at 25° C. and 60 per cent relative humidity, when subjected to reciprocal light and dark periods.

The results of Experiments 10 and 11 show a similar relation between the light interval and periodicity. The curves for Experiment 10 (Fig. 5) show that after the first opening movement in response to the temperature of the experimental chambers, there was a gradual closing both in light and darkness. When the lighting was reversed at midnight there was a slow opening in light and closing in darkness, showing the weakening of the periodic effect by the disturbed rhythm which the flowers had undergone during the preceding 18 hours. The next light reversal, at noon, resulted in somewhat erratic movements. The flowers used in Experiment 11 were placed in the experimental chambers at noon. These flowers showed distinctly the stimulating effect of light by expanding more rapidly and to a greater degree when illuminated than when in darkness, and the erratic behavior indicated the disturbance of the normal periodic cycle.

The flowers in Experiment 12 were subjected to light and dark periods of variable length, and responded by very erratic behavior which after the first 24 hours of the experiment showed little effect of normal periodicity. Here, as in the previous work, the usual periodic cycle disappeared after 24 hours under conditions in which the normal daily light and dark period was disturbed.

Tulip flowers kept at 25° and 60 per cent humidity respond to light by opening under increased intensity, and by closing when subjected to darkness. This effect results only in slight opening or closing when the changes are between 40 foot-candles and darkness, unless the direction of the movement agrees with that of the periodic behavior. After 24 hours exposure to abnormal light-dark periods, the periodic movements are disturbed and weakened.

EFFECTS OF HUMIDITY

The comparatively small amount of experimental work which has been reported on the effects of humidity on flowers of *Tulipa gesneriana* has uniformly given negative results. A series of experiments in which only the humidity varied was carried out along the lines of the preceding work. Table 3 gives the averages obtained.

The averages of five flowers, each at 25°, darkness, and 65 and 90 per cent relative humidity, are given in Experiment 13. These flowers had opened for the first time during the daylight period preceding the experiment, and when cut were placed immediately in the ecostat chambers. They carried out normal movements when returned to the bed the day following the close of the experiment.

These results show that the flowers opened and remained open during the experiment. Although there is no apparent difference in rate of opening at the different humidities, the final degree of expansion is inversely proportional to the humidity. The average maximum angular opening for the series was 156.3 for flowers at 65 per cent, and 130 at 90 per cent.

Experiment 14 gives the average percentage opening of five tulip flowers observed from 12 midnight in each of the ecostat chambers maintained at 25°, darkness, and 65 and 90 per cent relative

TABLE 3

TULIPA GESNERIANA

Behavior (percentage open) of flowers subjected to constant conditions of 25°C., darkness, and various relative humidities.

Experiment No.	13	14	15	13	14	15
Humidity %	90	90	100	65	65	65
Time						
9 p.m.	12.1			14.8		
12 m.	56.1	6.9		50.6	12.2	
3 a.m.	57.5	50.4		59.5	62.2	
6	69.1	56.7	18	78.7	77	10.8
9	82.1	58.1	85.5	87.5	85.4	85.8
11	64.1	56.7	69.8	84.1	83.7	96.7
2 p.m.	81.4	65.1	72.9	98.5	84.5	93.2
4	88.2	61.6	73.2	87.5	90	85.4
6	92.3	62.3	71.8	96.4	93.1	77.5
8	91.6	79.9	69.8	103.9	101.5	76.5
10	89.6	61.6	71.6	101.9	102.8	69.6
2 a.m.	88.9	65.8	82.4	104.7	90.9	85.8
6	86.7	79.8	95.8	108.7	106.8	96.7

humidity. The flowers were handled as in the preceding experiment, and checked similarly for normal behavior the following day. The average maximum angular opening of the perianth parts was 161° at 65 per cent humidity, and 123° at 90 per cent humidity. It will be seen that while the general opening reaction is similar in both chambers, the degree of opening is inversely proportional to the humidity of the air to which the flowers were exposed. Although considerable variation is shown, there is no evidence of periodicity.

Experiment 15 shows the results obtained with flowers cut at 6 A.M. and kept at 25°, darkness, and 65 and 100 per cent humidity. The flowers were selected and treated as described for the comparative experiments. The average maximum angular opening was 133.8 for flowers at 65 per cent humidity, and 124 for those at 100 per cent humidity. The results show that when placed in the chambers the flowers responded similarly by an immediate opening, and that this opening continued to a higher degree under conditions of low humidity rather than high. The initial opening movement was succeeded in the afternoon by a partial closing action which was followed by expansion continuing to the end of the experiment.

Tulip flowers are affected by atmospheric humidity. The magnitude of angular opening is increased at 65 per cent humidity, as compared to 90 per cent, at 25° and darkness. This effect of lower humidity values is probably connected with the water relations of the flower, and through this with the turgidity conditions operative in the movements of the perianth. Atmospheric humidity probably is not one of the factors which determine or predetermine periodicity of movement.

TISSUE STUDIES

Farmer (1902) has shown that turgidity changes in sections of the perianth of tulip can produce movements similar to those of the opening and closing of the flower. In experiments to confirm this, longitudinal sections through an open tulip flower exhibited a closing movement when placed in distilled water at 20°. In similar treatment of sections made through a closed flower a closing movement still occurred, bringing the perianth parts into a curved position mechanically impossible in the entire flower. This movement required about one hour at 20°. When such sections, or similar portions, of normally closed flowers were placed in an .1M solution of sucrose at 20°, the perianth parts slowly spread. This expansion occurred more rapidly when the sections were placed in stronger solutions. Molar sucrose solution produced complete opening in one hour and fifty minutes. Plate 2 shows sections treated as here described.

If we assume the impermeability of the cells to their solutes and to sucrose, which seems permissible from studies made by others, the effect of a hypertonic sucrose solution would be the withdrawal of water from the tissue, and this makes comprehensible the effect of reduced atmospheric humidity on the opening of the flower.

Sections through tulip flowers were placed in petri dishes and covered with distilled water or with various sucrose solutions, and the angles of the perianth tips were measured by means of a protractor after two hours at 20° when all movement had ceased. These equilibrium positions were : distilled water, −180°; sucrose solutions .1M 40°; .2M, 75°; .5M, 130°; 1M, 165°. If the curve of these values is plotted against the molarity and extended it will be seen to approach the 180° angle of opening, which in the variety here used (Darwin) is full expansion, asymptotically (Fig. 6). The osmotic pressure of the sucrose solution indicated as necessary for completely opening the perianth is thus something over 30 atmospheres.

Plasmolytic determinations at 20° were made on the tissue at the base of the perianth by means of freshly prepared c.p. sucrose solutions. A solution of .7 molar concentration was hypertonic to the parenchymatous cells, but no gradient could be observed between the outer and inner sides of the sections made across the perianth parts while these were opening or closing. This was perhaps due, at least partly, to the fact that the cells at the surface of the section, which had been necessarily injured in the process of sectioning, prevented a clear view of the deeper and more normal layers. There was great variation between the concentration of adjacent cells, those lying near the bundles being plasmolyzed by weaker solutions than were effective on the more distant portions of the tissue.

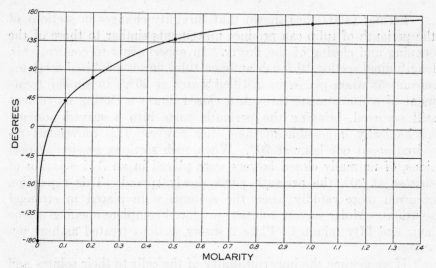

Fig. 6.—The relation, in sections of flowers of *Tulipa gesneriana*, between the position of the perianth and the concentrations of sucrose solutions with which they are in equilibrium at 20° C.

Since the epidermal layers can be quickly removed intact, and are in contact with the tissues on the opposite sides of the perianth, they offer a means for the comparative study of changes in osmotic concentration taking place during flower movement. A large number of plasmolysis determinations were made under the conditions given above, on the epidermal cells taken from opposite sides of the basal portion of the perianth. Solutions which just produced incipient plasmolysis in most cells after 5 minutes were: closed flower, outer .9 M, inner .8 M at 7 to 7:30 A.M; .75 M in both inner and outer epidermis when the flowers were opening at 8:30 to 9 A.M.; and .65 M and .75 M for these layers when the open flower was taken from the field at 10:30 A.M. When kept in the closed condition at 15° for 6 hours, the outer epidermis required .7 M solution for plasmolysis, and the inner .8 M at 3 P.M. After remaining open at 30°, 40 foot-candles, and 65 per cent humidity for 6 hours, the relations at 10 A.M. were: outer .7 M, inner .5 M.

The osmotic concentration of the epidermis on opposite surfaces

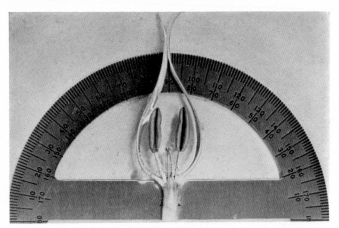

A. Normal closed flower

B. After 1 hour in .1M sucrose

C. After 20 minutes in water

Longitudinal sections of the flower of *Tulipa gesneriana* after treatment with sucrose solution of various osmotic concentration

of the perianth base of tulip flowers does not bear a constant relation to the position of the floral parts, but does indicate that variations in concentration of cell solutions precede and accompany flower movement. The concentration difference between the outer and inner epidermis does not exceed .2 M sucrose or 4.4 atmospheres pressure, and this is strikingly below the concentration required to force sections of the flower into the open position. Concentration changes accompanying flower movement are doubtless of greater magnitude in the deeper tissues of the perianth which are more actively concerned in movement than the epidermis.

It may be assumed from this result that changes in hydrostatic pressure in the cells of perianth parts do not occur as rapidly as do the changes in osmotic pressure of the cell sap. This may be attributable to the rate at which underlying tissues supply water to the parts studied. An explanation also may be sought in the changes known to occur in the colloidal materials of the cells which are known to influence water retention and the rate of water movement between the cells of a tissue or adjacent tissues. This assumption is not unwarrantable, from results obtained with other flowers.

SUMMARY

Tulip flowers open in the morning and close in the late or early afternoon, depending upon the intensity of the factors which favor evaporation. While air temperature and light intensity are rising at the time of opening, and falling during the closing period, and atmospheric humidity is varying inversely, no close correlation could be found between the time or rate of movement and the intensity of these factors in the field. No relation between floral transpiration and the stage of opening was found. The water content of the basal portion of the perianth parts is high before the opening of the flower, and decreases as the closing time is approached. Field experiments showed the reaction of flowers to temperature changes, but did not disclose a response to light or to atmospheric humidity.

Laboratory studies carried out under constant conditions revealed a slight periodic opening during the morning and closing in the afternoon at temperatures of $20°$, $25°$, and $30°$, but this behavior largely disappeared after one day of these unvarying conditions. The periodicity rhythm is predetermined by the variations in light and temperature of the preceding day, and is largely suppressed at a temperature of $15°$. When changes between $15°$ and $30°$ are used as stimuli, periodicity is shown by the reactions which attain maximum rate and extent only when corresponding in direction with it. Tulip flowers open in response to a rise in temperature, and close with a fall between $15°$ and $30°$. If periodic conditions are similar, the degree of expansion of flowers varies with the temperature. Opening reactions follow changes from darkness to light of 40 foot-candles intensity, but such a stimulus is not effective when opposed to periodic tendencies. Laboratory experiments clearly indicate that the response to stimuli, as measured by the rate of reaction, is predetermined. This predetermination is largely a result of light variations as they occur in the field. Exposure of the flowers to abnormal light intervals disturbs the normal rhythm. When opening occurs at atmospheric humidities of 65 to 100 per cent, the degree of expansion to which it attains varies inversely with the humidity values. The perianth parts in longitudinal sections of the flower placed in sucrose solution assume an angle which is directly proportional to the sugar concentration. Plasmolytic determinations show that variations in osmotic concentration occur in the tissues concerned in movement during the daily behavior cycle of the flower. Osmotic concentrations in the tulip flower, as determined by plasmolysis, are not very different from those obtained by Guttenberg in *Dionaea muscipula* (1925).

TARAXACUM OFFICINALE

FIELD BEHAVIOR

The heads of *Taraxacum officinale* are protected by a double layer of involucral bracts until they emerge above the surface of the ground, but very soon after the appearance of the elliptical green bud, this calyculus is reflexed and never again shows movement during the period of development of the flower and fruit. Since the rate of bud development depends upon environmental conditions, records were kept both in Colorado Springs, Colorado, and Tucson, Arizona, of the development of over a hundred flowers in typical habitats among herbaceous vegetation and during different portions of the flowering season.

The following are averages for ten heads on successive days, from April 26 to May 23, of the length (in millimeters) of the peduncle from the time of the emergence of the bud above the rosette to the collapse of the peduncle after seed dispersal. The letters following the measurements indicate the following: *o*, first opening of the flower; *s*, peduncle straightening after the flowering period; *x*, peduncles straight, bracts reflexed, and parachutes expanded. These averages are: 7.1, 15.1, 25.2, 30.7, 50.6, 61.5, 100.2*o*, 111.8, 115.8, 117.5, 118.8, 122, 125.2, 129.2, 131.1, 133.1, 135, 137.1, 144.1, 151.1, 155.1, 177, 260*s*, 326*x*, 374, 392.5, 395.6, 401.7.

At this season the plants required nearly thirty days for the floral life history, but this time was reduced to twelve days during hot dry periods. When growing in open soil fully exposed to the sun the peduncles often remain as short as two centimeters, but in dense shade final lengths as great as 90 centimeters have been observed. The growth curves vary in degree rather than in form, and show two grand periods of elongation; one immediately preceding the opening of the flower, and the second of greater rate and extent just prior to the release of the achenes. The two regions of greatest elongation lie just below the bracts and near the base of the peduncle.

When the buds first emerge above the rosette of leaves they are tomentose and frequently the peduncles are flattened, but later the hairy covering is lost and the form of the peduncle approaches the cylindrical. At the close of the flowering period the peduncle bends downward in a sigmoid curve, lowering the head but maintaining it in a vertical position. Later during the second grand period of elongation the peduncle again straightens. Shortly after this the involucral bracts are reflexed preparatory to seed dispersal, and 24 to 48 hours later the peduncle bends over and collapses. Premature removal of the fruit does not alter this behavior.

Following the pre-floral period of pedunclar growth, the bracts of the involucre are reflexed by a curvature in the basal region, and the outer flowers of the head open, the ligules bending outward and unrolling. During the cooler portions of the flowering season the heads commonly remain open throughout the daylight period of three to five successive days, showing a decreasing cluster of unopened flowers closely packed in the center of the disk. With the advance of the season this process occurs more rapidly, so that in late July at Colorado Springs the heads are seldom open for more than two successive days. During the warm dry season the heads open by 6 A.M. and close by 9 A.M., but this behavior may be modified if the flowers grow in a shady moist habitat, or if the plants have been delayed in blooming by mowing on a well watered lawn, when the closing is retarded. During rainy, cloudy, or foggy weather, heads may continue open until late afternoon, and flowers growing in cool shaded locations may remain entirely closed.

Frequently heads open asymmetrically, due to injuries caused by attacks of insects or of fungi, or to unequal exposure of the different portions of the head to radiant energy and the consequent thermal effects. In the former case, portions of the heads are permanently prevented from opening, but in the latter merely delayed. When once the opening or closing reaction is under way, observation and timing disclosed no difference in rate which could be correlated with the conditions of the habitat. Since the experimental data which follow apply with much greater accuracy to this point than the field observations, the latter are omitted here. Plate 3 shows stages in the floral life history.

EFFECTS OF AGE

The angle between the involucral bracts at full opening increased with the age of the heads of *Taraxacum officinale* but the movement was accompanied by the opening of the mature flowers and was a convenient measure of the opening process. The angles of the involucre, measured daily at Colorado Springs, June 14-21, showed as an average of ten heads, the following maxima: −60° (closed buds), 41° (buds slightly open), 120° (outer three rows of flowers open), 155° (flowers opening toward center of head and aging at outside), 163° (20 per cent of the flowers still unexpanded), 202° (flowers open to center, flower of outer half of head old), 281° (flowers old except at center), −26° (heads old and closed).

The comparative age of heads may be estimated accurately by

PLATE 3

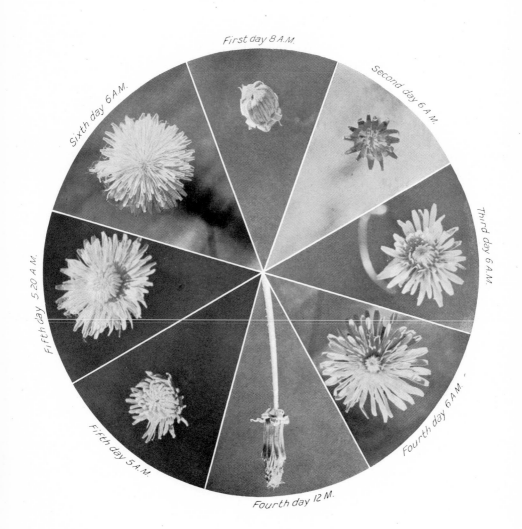

Flower cycle of *Taraxacum officinale*

the angular opening of the involucre, and also by the number of buds at the center. Old heads which have nearly all the flowers inactive do not open as early in the day as do the younger, and commonly close after the latter. Frequently old heads do not open fully on the last day of their activity, but closure is complete. The involucral bracts sometimes open one or two days after the permanent closing of all the flowers.

MEASUREMENT OF FACTORS IN THE FIELD

Conclusions as to the causative factors either of opening or closing of the heads of *Taraxacum officinale* cannot be drawn safely from field observations alone. The absolute effect of such factors at the time of or immediately before the reaction of the flower varies with the preceding conditions of the habitat in which the plant has been growing, with the age and physiological condition of the individual, and with other variables. Factors are in a state of constant flux, and it is difficult to ascertain from field measurements even the physical effects of a factor on a flower, such, for instance, as the absorption of radiant energy by flowers of different colors, textures, and angles of exposure. Only the most general conclusions can be drawn from field observations, and these to the best advantage when single inflorescences are observed.

Table 4 gives a few typical results obtained by factor readings made in as close proximity as possible to the inflorescence under observation, at the time of the first observable opening and the first closing movement. Although there is great variability in the factor readings at the time of movement, it will be seen that during the early season at Colorado Springs the flowers open in the morning when the temperature is rising, and close in the afternoon when it is falling. But later in the flowering period both in Colorado and in Arizona, closing occurs earlier in the day, and under higher temperature and lower humidity than that which obtained at the time of opening. Thus, early in the flowering season at Colorado Springs, heads remain open throughout the day and close at sundown, but later in the year they close during the midforenoon. Observations at Tucson late in March show that heads open and close at that season in Arizona in much the way here described as typical for Colorado in July. In June, at the Alpine Laboratory (8300 feet), *Taraxacum* heads which do not receive direct sunlight are delayed in opening, and remain closed during the entire day if low temperature conditions obtain. Thus on June 24, 1924, heads exposed to direct sunlight near the Alpine Laboratory opened fully by 6 A.M., while those shaded by vegetation remained closed. The appearance

TABLE 4

Taraxacum Officinale

Field conditions at the time of opening and closing of flowers.

Colorado Springs, April.

Flowers Opening				Flowers Closing			
Time	Temp. °C.	Humidity %	Light Conditions	Time	Temp. °C.	Humidity %	Light Conditions
A.M.				P.M.			
6:20	14.3	58	Sun	5	11.4	50	Shade
7:25	13.5	60	"	5:15	12.4	55	"
7:30	14	54	"	5:45	11.7	70	"
7:40	12.9	65	"	5:50	12.6	62	"
8	13.4	50	"	6:10	12.3	62	"
8:20	13.6	66	"	6:20	13.7	60	"
8:30	14.2	68	"	6:20	13	43	"
8:35	13.6	65	"	6:30	13.3	60	"
8:40	14	57	"	6:30	12.4	74	"
8:40	12.5	70	"	6:50	13.1	55	"
Ave. 7:58	13.6	61.3		6:03	12.59	59.1	
A.M.				A.M.			
4:20	16	63	Sun	10:10	26	24	Sun
4:30	14	60	Partial Sun	10:20	18.6	49	"
4:45	18	63	Sun	10:30	21	27	"
4:45	16	54	"	10:30	28	19	"
4:50	19	49	"	10:35	18.5	44	"
4:55	20.1	28	Partial Sun	10:35	23	34	Shade
5	20.2	45	"　　"	10:40	25	14	Sun
5:05	22	28	Sun	10:40	26	25	"
5:10	19.5	44	"	10:50	28	21	"
5:20	16	65	"	10:50	27.5	15	"
Ave. 4:53	17.98	50.9		10:34	24.16	27.2	
A.M.				A.M.			
5	10.4	60	Sun	9:10	19.5	32	Sun
5:20	7.3	50	"	9:20	19.8	30	"
5:20	9.5	46	"	9:25	19.4	35	"
5:50	8.2	58	"	9:30	20.2	35	"
5:50	9.8	60	"	9:35	20	38	"
6	8.5	65	"	9:40	20.5	28	"
6:20	10.5	48	"	9:40	20.5	28	"
6:30	10.2	32	"	9:40	21	30	"
6:40	11	45	"	9:50	19	36	"
6:40	10.7	45	"	10:10	21.3	25	"
Ave. 5:57	9.66	52.9		9:36	20.12	31.7	

of fog at 7:20 A.M. held the temperature at 14°–15° and the humidity at 89–95 per cent. The shaded heads remained partly open in the morning, but closed in the afternoon.

Hygrothermograph records made in the field adjacent to the *Taraxacum* heads under observation have the same limitations as those discussed in connection with the intermittent observations of tulips, given in Table 4. The records merely serve to show that during the early part of the summer *Taraxacum* heads commonly open during a period of rapidly rising temperature, increasing light intensity, and falling humidity in the morning, and close in a period of falling temperature and light intensity, and rising humidity in the afternoon. Later in the summer they close with rising temperature and light intensity, and falling humidity, in the morning.

Heads exposed to conditions promoting evaporation, wind, etc., commonly close in summer before those not so exposed. This effect is not noticeable during the early flowering season. Transpiration studies were made by cutting heads of similar age and peduncle length under water and placing them in vials of water sealed with plasticine. Ten of these potometers comprising a battery were weighed singly on a quantitative balance, the bottles fixed in a vertical position, and exposed in sunny habitats where the behavior of the undisturbed heads furnished a criterion of normal action with which to compare the experimental material. Evaporation from free water surface of approximately 30 sq. cm. was determined by exposing water in a blackened metal pan 10 cm. in diameter and 8 mm. deep, to the conditions in the immediate vicinity of each battery. Readings were made every two hours. During the time required for weighing, the entire battery and evaporation pan were kept in the laboratory.

The results show great variability. The averages during June show an increasing rate of transpiration from 6 A.M. to 4 P.M. During this period the heads opened and closed. Heads exposed to full sun showed about double the transpiration rate of those in shaded habitats. No change due to the degree of closure of the heads is evident in the transpiration rate. On June 14, experiments at Colorado Springs gave an average hourly transpiration rate of .03 and .02 grams in sun and shade respectively between 6 and 8 A.M., and .12 and .06 grams between 12 and 3 P.M. The results when compared with the evaporation from a free water surface showed no close correlation with flower movement. This may be due to the difficulty of obtaining a standard exposure when battery and pan were both placed among vegetation which even when not casting shade upon the experimental material causes unknown and variable thermal and wind effects. Any reduction in transpiration caused by closure of the heads is obscured by the variability of results and by increased intensity of conditions which promote rapid desiccation. Any transpirational effects due to flower position are too small to be ascertained by the methods used.

A study was made of the water content of the heads and of various parts apparently concerned in opening and closing. Buds were labeled before the first opening and observed daily. On May 5, heads which had been open one daily period May 4 were selected, the desired parts removed and placed immediately in a weighed vial with a rubber stopper. After weighing, all were dried to a constant weight at 100°, cooled over calcium chloride, and reweighed. The results are given in Table 5. The material was collected when the first sign of the opening or closing movement, as given in the fifth column, was observed. The percentage water content is the loss at 100° based on the original weight.

TABLE 5

TARAXACUM OFFICINALE

Water content (percentage loss in original weight at 100°) of heads at opening and closing period (the beginning of these processes).

Date	Time	Part Used	Number Averaged	Condition	Water Content%	Locality
May 5	8 a.m.	Head	10	Opening	85.1	Colo. Springs, Colo.
5	2:30 p.m.	Head	10	Closing	81.4	" " "
5	8 a.m.	Flowers	50	Opening	84.2	" " "
5	2:30 p.m.	Flowers	50	Closing	82.9	" " "
5	8 a.m.	Involucre	25	Opening	83.9	" " "
5	2:30 p.m.	Involucre	25	Closing	83.3	" " "
6	8 a.m.	Base of flowers	50	Opening	85	" " "
6	2:20 p.m.	Base of flowers	50	Closing	80	" " "
6	8 a.m.	Base of involucre	30	Opening	84.3	" " "
6	2:20 p.m.	Base of involucre	35	Closing	83.4	" " "
June 10	6 a.m.	Head	20	Opening	83.8	" " "
10	9:45 a.m.	Head	20	Closing	80.7	" " "
March 12	7 a.m.	Involucre	25	Opening	85.8	Tucson, Arizona.
12	8:45 a.m.	Involucre	25	Closing	82.4	" "
12	3:30 p.m.	Involucre	25	Closed	81.3	" "
14	3 p.m.	Involucre	25	Closed	80.5	" "
14	10:15 a.m.	Involucre	25	Full open	83.9	" "
15	7 a.m.	Involucre	20	Opening	84.4	" "
15	7 a.m.	Flowers	50	Opening	83	" "
15	7 a.m.	Flowers	50	Opening	87.4	" "
16	7:30 a.m.	Flowers	50	Opening	85.5	" "
16	3 p.m.	Flowers	50	Closed	83.7	" "

It will be seen that, although the water content was variable, it was lower at the time of closing than at that of opening, in the entire heads as well as in the parts more actively concerned. Thus, the average difference in percentage water content between the opening and closing conditions of comparable flowers was 3.4 for entire heads, 1.5 for entire flowers, 2 for the entire involucre, and 5 and .9 respectively for the basal portion of the flower and involucre. Sections of bracts of *Taraxacum* exhibited movements comparable to the opening of the head if placed in distilled water for an hour at 20°, and were closed partly by .5M sucrose solution in 2 hours. Flowers were more easily affected, .1M sucrose producing the rolling up of the ligule in 15 minutes at 20°. The flowers were not curved in, even by treatment with saturated sucrose solution at 20°. The flower movements of *Taraxacum,* as well as those of *Tulipa,* are intimately connected with the water relations of the tissues. The fact that the sections of *Tulipa* close in water, *and those of Taraxacum* open, indicates a difference in permeability rather than in the water relations of the flower. Flower movement has slight effect, if any, on the transpiration rate, the water content following the daily cycle of evaporation.

FIELD EXPERIMENTS

Adjacent plants of *Taraxacum officinale* were covered with bell jars provided with thermometers and dew-point tubes, and with heated or cooled air forced in as described in Chapter II. Although constant temperatures could not be maintained, a considerable temperature difference was produced, and after an initial period of stabilization these temperatures followed the same general course of variation. Table 6 gives a set of typical results from this work, from which it will be seen that heads in the heated jar opened nearly 30 minutes before those in the cooled chamber. It was found generally possible to open the heads in this way if the experiments were carried out before the flowers had passed through their normal daily opening. When open flowers were subjected to similar conditions, the heads in the heated atmosphere closed before those in the cooled. Experiments of the same nature begun in the afternoon after the heads had closed for the day were unsuccessful in producing another opening.

Shade tents of approximately 50 and 100 per cent efficiency produced no change in the time of opening other than that which could

TABLE 6

TARAXACUM OFFICINALE

Experimental field behavior.

Bell Jar No. 1				Bell Jar No. 2		
Time	Temp.°C.	Humidity %	Response	Temp.°C.	Humidity %	Response
A.M.						
9:15	14.5	42	Closed	14.2	44	Closed
9:23	15.5	60	Closed	12	58	Closed
9:27	17	66	Closed	12.4	65	Closed
9:30	18.5	68	Closed	12.5	66	Closed
9:35	20	68	Closed	12.2	68	Closed
9:38	20.5	67	Involucre spreading	12.5	69	Closed
9:40	20.5	66	Rays opening	12.6	69	Closed
9:50	21.5	59	Rays open	12.7	65	Closed
10	22	55	Fully open	13	62	Beginning to open

be attributed to the thermal effects. Thus, if plants were enclosed, before the normal opening cycle, in tents made of black rubber cloth, the temperature was increased considerably and the flowers responded by opening. Lighter shade produced by a ventilated cloth tent delayed opening and closing slightly, and also maintained a lower temperature than that normally present in the adjacent field.

Taraxacum heads are normally directed upward, or toward the source of maximum illumination. Hence experiments were undertaken to determine any change in behavior which might result from unequal illumination. Heads were clamped to a small wooden support and placed so that the sunlight was received either directly on the involucre, or at right angles to the longitudinal axis of the head. Heads placed in both of these positions before the daily expansion period were slightly delayed in the time of opening, but showed no effect in closing time. When buds which had not previously been open were exposed laterally, the bracts and flowers on the more strongly illuminated side opened before the rest. Inverted heads were not delayed in opening, and expanded symmetrically. If closed heads were exposed shortly before the normal opening time to a current of air heated to 50° by passage through a metal tube suspended over a flame, they opened asymmetrically, the side receiving the warm air expanding first.

Shortly before the time of the normal daily expansion, closed flowers of *Taraxacum* may be stimulated to open by exposure to sunlight or to a current of warm air, and in this response react independently of the other flowers or bracts of the head which are not stimulated.

To check any alterations in flower behavior due to changed water relations of the plant, several field experiments were made. A group of plants growing with many others in a moderately dry meadow at Colorado Springs were irrigated daily sufficiently to cover the surface to a depth of one inch, the amount being applied slowly and in the evening in order to reduce run-off and evaporation. Daily watering was continued from June 5 to 19, but no difference could be seen in the opening or closing time of the flowers in the irrigated and unirrigated groups. Disturbing the water relations of the plants by oiling the surface of the leaves did not change the flower behavior, nor were alterations of movement produced by injection of water into the peduncle or receptacle, or by supplying the cut peduncle with .2M sucrose solution.

The water relations which may be responsible for the opening and closing of *Taraxacum* heads are independent within wide limits of those of the rest of the plant.

Cutting produced no immediate effect in the reaction of the flower; heads cut in any manner and with varying lengths of peduncle responded like uncut heads if exposed in the habitat. Even when the heads were severed close below the involucre and were exposed in the field, the flowers opened at the normal time, often incompletely, but closed prematurely in a partly withered condition. The reactions of cut heads which had been supplied with water often became erratic after 50 hours, especially if kept at a temperature of 25° or higher. The removal of the flowers from the head caused an immediate partial closure of the involucre due to the flattening of the receptacle, but the bracts carried out their normal movement cycle on the following day, and then remained closed. The removal of the involucre, even before the first opening of the bud, produced no marked change in the behavior of the flowers except that the closure of the head was incomplete, showing that the bracts were without significant effect on the behavior of the flower other than as a mechanical aid to complete closing. Separate flowers removed from the head may be activated to movements corresponding to opening and closing, by submergence in water or sucrose solution. Figure 7 shows a flower in the positions assumed, 1 as removed from the closed head, 2 after

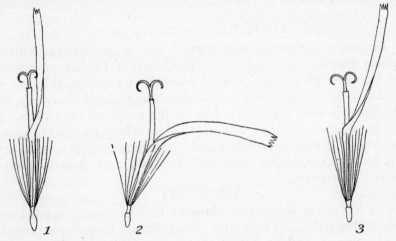

Fig. 7.—Positions assumed by the corolla of *Taraxacum officinale* in water and in sucrose solution.

twenty minutes immersion in distilled water at 20°, and 3 after a further immersion of one hour in 4M sucrose solution at 20°. It is evident that changes in the water relations of the tissues of the flower may produce movements similar to those of opening and closing.

Field studies show that during the early part of the flowering season, the heads of *Taraxacum* open in the morning shortly after sunrise and remain thus throughout the day, but that later in the season they open at or before sunrise and close during the forenoon. Opening occurs under rising temperature and light intensity and falling humidity, but is not correlated with any one of these factors; closing may occur under either rising or falling temperature and light. On cool days with overcast skies the flowers may remain closed. Individual flowers or bracts in a head will open in response to sunlight or heated air, independently of the response of adjacent organs. Although the water content of the head and of the motile structures is lower at the time of closing than when the opening movement is taking place, there is no apparent correlation between this difference and the activity of the flower part, and no apparent connection between the flower movement and the water relations of the plant. *Taraxacum* flowers respond to temperature changes, and possibly also to those of light, but only when the periodic and stimulated responses agree in direction. The involucral bracts carry out normal movements on the day following the removal of the flowers, and the removal of the involucre does not materially change flower movement. Separate flowers may be stimulated to movements corresponding to those of opening and closing, by placing them in water or in strong solutions of sucrose.

LABORATORY EXPERIMENTS

Ecostat experiments were carried out in accordance with the methods described in Chapter II. The heads of *Taraxacum officinale* used for experiment were selected carefully for comparable age and habitat. Some of the work was done at the Alpine Laboratory, 8300 feet, which is near the upper limit of the range of *Taraxacum*, and some at Colorado Springs, 2000 feet below, where the plants grow in abundance. It was frequently possible to make simultaneous observations on heads collected from both habitats, and thus to compare behavior differences.

PERIODICITY

Table 7 gives the results obtained under constant conditions of temperature, light, and humidity, with different treatments preceding the experiment, and at different temperature levels. These values are the average percentage opening of five to ten heads of *Taraxacum officinale,* and have been confirmed by other experiments the results of which are not given. Flowers of comparable age were selected during the open period on the day preceding the experiment. Constant conditions of darkness and 50 per cent humidity were maintained. The results given in columns *a* were obtained from plants growing at Colorado Springs at an altitude of 6000 feet; those in columns *b* from heads flowering at the Alpine Laboratory at an altitude of 8300 feet.

TABLE 7

TARAXACUM OFFICINALE

Behavior (average percentage opening) of flowers (5 to 10) from different habitats when subjected to constant conditions of 15° to 35° C., darkness, and 50% humidity.

a. Colorado Springs, Colorado, 6000 feet.
b. Alpine Laboratory, Colorado, 8300 feet.

Habitat	b	a	b	a	a	a	a	a	b	a	a	a	a	b	b	a	a	a
Temp. °C.	10	15	15	15	15	20	20	20	20	25	25	25	25	25	30	35	35	35
Time																		
12 mt	2	4	2						5					8	2			
12:30						4				4						6		
1 a.m.	2	4	2			4			5	4				8	2	9		
2	2	6	2			4			1	7				5	5	8		
3	2	6	2			6	11		1	8	7			12	20	6	12	
4	2	7	2			5	22		15	11	37			18	38	6	23	
5	2	8	2			9	34		23	18	38			23	50	1	22	
6	3	8	2	10		18	40	30	36	32	62	16		25	58	0	22	35
7	3	9	10	27		41	55	57	60	43	65	56		47	70	0	17	100
8	3	10	26	32		51	65	70	65	54	64	73		45	70	0	15	94
9	3	16	77	40		56	73	75	65	48	55	66		45	70	0	15	98
10	3	20	77	45		54	78	72	65	43	46	46		45	50	0	15	84
11	3	20	77	34		52	60	70	65	31	32	35		40	15	0	15	76
12 m.	3	18	77	27	63	44	44	64	60	27	26	26	55	40	15	0	11	65
1 p.m.	3	17	54	21	26	33	27	52	55	20	19	17	22	40	15	0	7	54
2	3	13	50	20	9	14	14	44	45	15	13	14	10	40	15	0	7	43
3	2	12	34	14	5	13	12	33	10	13	13	13	8	10	0	0	7	36
4	2	19	20	6	3	14	8	24	10	11	11	8	5	10	0	0	7	33
5	2	8	13	6	3	8	8	12	5	9	9	5	3	10	0	0	7	26
6	2	3	10	2	3	8	8	11	2	8	7	3	3	0	0	0	7	21
7	2	2	6	2	2				2		3	2	2	0	0			
8	2	2	4	2	2				2		3	2	2	0	0			
9	2	2	2	2	2				2					0	0			
10	2	2	2	2	2				2					0	0			
11	2	2	2	2	2				2					0	0			
12 mt.	2	2	2	2	2				2					0	0			
1 a.m.			2						2					0	0			
2			2						2					0	0			
3			2						6					0	0			
4			2						6					0	0			
5			2						6					0	0			
6			6						6					0	0			
7			17						6					0	0			
8			77						6					0	0			
9			77						15					0	0			
10			77						15					0	0			
11			77						15					0	0			
12 m.			77						0					0	0			
1 p.m.			43						0					0	0			
2			43						0					0	0			
3			33						0					0	0			
4			16						0					0	0			
5			12															
6			8															

Some of the typical curves are shown in Figure 8. The results show that periodicity is conspicuous in the opening of the heads in every case except at temperatures of 10° to 35°, the heads opening in the morning and closing from mid-forenoon to 6 P.M. At the different temperature levels the extent of opening varied, but there is no apparent relation between these temperatures and the time of movement. Similarly, the time at which the heads were placed in the experimental chambers—that is, the time of exposure to field conditions—produced a marked effect on the extent of the reaction, but little on the time at which it occurred. Thus at 15°, 20°, 25°, and 30°, the opening movement usually began between 2 and 3 A.M. in any set of heads in the ecostat chambers at this time. A temperature of 10° entirely prevented a reaction, hence the results show no periodic influences. At 35° a slight opening reaction followed immediately after the stimulus resulting from placing the flowers in the chamber, and this was at once succeeded by complete and permanent closing.

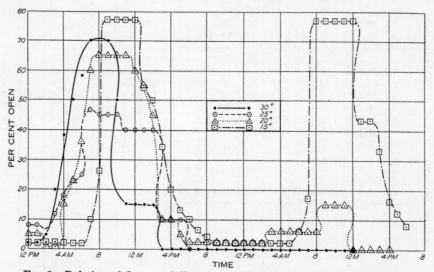

FIG. 8.—Relation of flowers of *Taraxacum officinale* to constant temperatures.

The effect of periodicity on movement is also shown by computing the hourly rate of movement after the flowers were placed in the constant temperature chambers. It is realized that the time-temperature relation would alter the results, but one hour after the beginning of treatment is considered significant. The results of this computation are given in Table 9. They show that the rate of movement depends on the time in the daily periodic cycle when the stimulation is applied, but that this is greatly altered by temperature.

Thus, at 15°, 20°, and 25° the rate of opening reached its maximum at 6 A.M., while at 30° and 35° it was attained at 3 A.M. Irrespective of the time of occurrence, the maximum hourly rate of opening as affected by temperature shows a characteristic "grand period" curve, the rate values being 0, 10.7, 22.2, 24.3, 18, and 5.5, for 10°, 15°, 20°, 25°, 30°, and 35° respectively. The time the flowers began to respond by closing was in inverse relation to temperature, occurring at 6 A.M. at 35°, 9 A.M. at 30° and 25°, and 12 M. at 20° and 15°. The effect of temperature on the maximum hourly rate of closing allows no generalization such as that given for the opening response.

TABLE 8

TARAXACUM OFFICINALE

Behavior (percentage open) of flowers subjected to changes between 15° and 30° C., after different storage conditions.

    c. heads stored 3 hours in Dewar flask, at 4°, darkness and 100% humidity before experiment.

    d. heads cut, supplied with water, and left 3 hours in habitat before experiment.

    x. changed from 15° to 30°.

    y. changed from 30° to 15°.

Temp. °C.	25	25	Alternating between 15° and 30°							
Time	c	d								
8 p.m.			13				12			
9			13				10			
10			10				7			
11			8				5			
12 mt.			0x	0			5y	2		
12:30	6									
1 a.m.	6		7	0			5	2		
2	6		100	0	3		2	12	5	
3	15	4	17	0x	3		2	30y	5	
4	43	37	33	67	3		2	50	5	
5	60	76	45	90	3		2	55	55	
6	68	84	45	97	3x		3	67	80y	20
7	77	89	45	97	83		17	87	87	75
8	76	100	20	97	90	100	63	90	85	80
9	61	85	10	95	90	100	74	100	80	90
10	46	70	7	90	87	100	78	100	76	94
11	38	37	0	67	87	100	87	95	70	100
12 m.	27	36	0	50	72	87	87	90	62	100y
1 p.m.	21	31		17	60	70	75	87	50	87
2	16	22		5	40	60	68	73	44	75
3	15	20		0	20	44x	50	60	40	47
4	14	17				40	44	54		20
5	12	12				23	32	31		17
6	8	6				18	20	12		13
7		2				10	20	7		8
8		2				9	18	6		3
9						7	15	2		0
10						0	10	2		0
11						0	9	2		
12 mt.							5	2		

The results given in column 2, Table 8, were obtained from heads
comparable in every way with those used for the results given in
Table 7, except that they were cut at 9 P.M. and placed with the
cut end in water in a Dewar flask kept at 4° and 100 per cent humidity. The heads used for the averages given in column d were similar,
but after cutting they were stored in the field near the undisturbed
heads used for the 25° 3 A.M. series of Table 7. The results show
that the amplitude rather than the periodicity of the movement was
affected. Although cut flowers exposed in the field showed a normal
response for 72 hours, Table 7 and Figure 8 indicate that this periodic
action is markedly affected at different temperature levels. Under
constant conditions of darkness and 50 per cent humidity the periodic
movements occurred on the second day at 15° with normal amplitude and at normal time; at 20° the movements of the second day
were displaced in time and greatly reduced in amplitude; and at 25°
and 30° the periodic movements of the second day were entirely suppressed. The periodicity of the flowers of *Taraxacum* depends on the
daily periodic cycle of the habitat factors, as Stoppel has shown for
the leaves of *Phaseolus,* but this effect may persist at least to the
second day under conditions of 15°, be weakened at 20°, or entirely
destroyed at 25° and 30°. Since a similar relation to the preceding
day factor-cycle is shown by the leaves of *Phaseolus,* and since connection with the plant shows little effect upon the periodicity of
Taraxacum heads, this behavior probably is due to the accumulation
of photosynthetic products which are not translocated but gradually
destroyed by oxidation in the active organs.

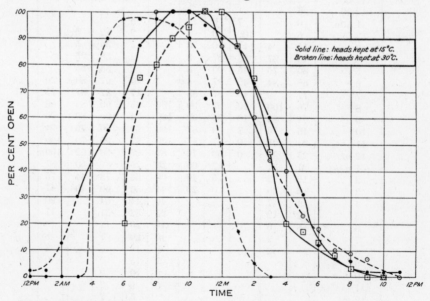

FIG. 9.—Relation of flowers of *Taraxacum officinale* to change in temperature.

Table 8 gives the floral reactions of selected heads. Under *c* are recorded the averages obtained from heads growing at Colorado Springs, which before the beginning of the experiment received three hours storage in a Dewar flask at 4°, darkness, and 100 per cent humidity. Under *d* are recorded the averages obtained from heads cut and left for three hours in the habitat, the cut peduncles being supplied with water. Temperature changes were made at the times indicated, by interchanging the heads between the 15° and 30° chambers. A change from 15° to 30° is indicated by *x*, the reverse direction by *y*.

The periodicity of the heads of *Taraxacum* is also shown by the movements resulting from a temperature stimulation. The results of a sudden temperature change between 15° and 30° are given in Table 8, and indicate that such a temperature change initiates or accelerates a movement only when acting in the direction of the periodic tendency of the time. Thus a change from 15° to 30° resulted in rapid opening when made at 3 or 6 A.M., slow expansion when made at 12 midnight, and only slight and temporary reduction in the rate of closing when made at 3 P.M. The closing reaction following a change from 30° to 15° did not occur when the change was made at 3 or 6 A.M., but resulted when the shift was made at noon. Typical results are graphed in Figure 9. Similar relations varying only in degree followed when the changes were between 15° and 25°, 15° and 20°, and 10° and these upper levels.

If the rate of flower movement for the hour following the temperature change is taken as a measure of the stimulated reaction, we have the values given in Table 9, in which the positive numbers indicate an opening movement and the negative a closing one. This table gives the rate of movement at various temperature stimulations and at various times during a daily movement cycle.

TABLE 9

Taraxacum Officinale

Behavior (hourly rate of opening and closing) of flowers following change to temperatures indicated, under constant conditions of darkness and 50% humidity.

Positive numbers: opening movement.
Negative numbers: closing movement.

Temp. °C.	10	20	10	30	15	20	15	25	15	30
Time										
12 mt.		17				6	0	3	0	7
3 a.m.	-10	45	-25	75		48	-15	58	0	67
6		85				54	-10	70	7	80
9				8			0			
12 m.									-3	
3 p.m.						-7		-4		-4

The rates at the same periods but at constant temperature levels
are graphed in Figure 10, and the difference between these values is
shown in Figure 11. The averages are computed partly from results
given in Tables 7 and 8, and partly from other experimental data
not given here in full. It will be seen that the maxima of reaction
rates are proportional to the temperatures of the chambers to which
the heads were transferred; thus in changes from 15° to 20°, 25°, and
30°, these rates were 54, 70, and 80, respectively.

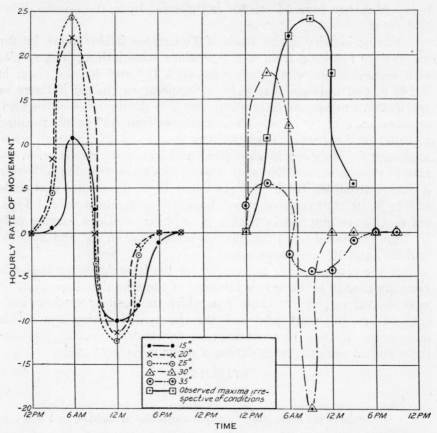

FIG. 10.—Hourly rate of opening and closing of flowers of *Taraxacum officinale*
under constant conditions of darkness and 50 per cent humidity.

If the differences are computed between the rates of movement
at constant temperatures similar to those to which the changes were
made, and the rate following the stimulus, the values represent the
reaction rates resulting from temperature change only. These values
are graphed in Figure 11, and show the great periodic change in
reaction rate during the day. The response to a change of 5°, 10°,
or 15°, was of a similar low value at midnight, increased markedly

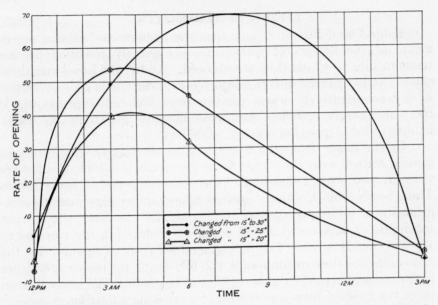

FIG. 11.—Stimulation rates of movement of flowers of *Taraxacum officinale* subjected to sudden changes of temperatures at different times of day.

at 3 A.M., decreased at the two lower temperature changes at 6 A.M., but increased for the higher, and fell to a common low level at 3 P.M.

Heads of *Taraxacum* show a daily cycle of periodic movement under constant conditions, opening in the morning and closing by evening. These movements did not appear at 10°, and were displaced and partly inhibited at 30° and 35°. At the higher temperatures, under conditions of darkness and 50 per cent humidity, periodic movements did not appear after 24 hours; at 15° they continued on the second day with little modification. Cutting and storage at low temperatures produced little effect on the periodic behavior. The hourly reaction rates show that both opening and closing maxima varied with the temperature at the lower levels, and that the time at which the maximum opening rate was attained and the closing movement began varied inversely with temperature. The response to temperature changes of constant magnitude shows a periodic relation, resulting in movement only when the reaction agrees with the periodic tendency. When the effects of different temperature levels were removed, the reactions to stimuli of constant magnitude as measured by the rate of movement showed maxima proportional to the temperature change at 3 A.M. and 6 A.M., and minimal opening rates at midnight. The same temperature stimulus which resulted in an opening movement at midnight, 3 A.M., and 6 A.M., initiated a closing reaction at 3 P.M.

EFFECTS OF TEMPERATURE

Table 7 and Figure 8 show that the opening and closing movements of the flowers of *Taraxacum* are greatly modified by the temperatures to which they are exposed. At 10° the heads remained closed; at 15° partial opening occurred in those which had developed in the comparatively warm conditions of Colorado Springs, 6,000 feet; and nearly complete expansion in those grown in the cooler habitat of the Alpine Laboratory, 8,300 feet.

In the heads from the lower habitat the degree of opening in general varied with the constant temperature to which the flowers were exposed, except that at 35° the curves dropped to lower levels. Thus, heads from Colorado Springs placed under experimental conditions near midnight, showed at 15°, 20°, 25°, and 35°, the average maximum expansions of 20, 56, 54, and 9, reached in the morning at 10, 9, 8, and 1 (Table 7). Dividing the extent of opening by the time gives the time-maxima of 2, 6.2, 6.7, and 9, for the temperatures in the order above; thus showing that in heads from the lower habitat there is a time-temperature relation for reaching a maximum opening which is directly proportional to the temperature.

Similar computations on heads from the Alpine Laboratory habitat give, for temperatures of 10°, 15°, 20°, 25°, and 30°, time-maxima of .5, 8.6, 8.1, 6.7 and 10. In this case the time-temperature relation is not dircet, the maxima being at 15° and 30°. But it is evident that there is a different time-temperature requirement for reaching maximum values in flowers growing in different ecological habitats. Thus at 15° the heads from Colorado Springs, at lower elevation, gave a time-maximum of 2, while those from the Alpine Laboratory habitat, at higher elevation, gave 8.6.

Rates of opening at constant temperatures, given in Table 7, further compared by computing those obtained from series started later in the day, show at 20°, 25°, and 35°, 11.2, 16.2, and 23 for the 3 A.M. series, and 25, 36.5, and 100 for the 6 A.M. series. At 15° the 6 A.M. series gives a value of 11.2, while the rate at 12 noon cannot be evaluated since the flowers were open when placed in the ecostat. The rate of opening is thus proportional to the temperature. If we consider the above values from the point of view of the beginning of the series, we have for 12 midnight, 3 A.M., and 6 A.M., 2, —, and 11.2 at 15°, 6.2, 11.2, and 25 at 20°, 6.8, 16.2, and 36.5 at 25°, and 9, 23, and 100 at 35°. The rate of opening thus shows not only a time-temperature relation, but also a relation to the time of day at which the heads were placed under experimental conditions.

If the closing rates are computed from the values given in Table 7 by dividing the difference between maximum and minimum expansion by the time required for the change, the relations are not as consistent for the closing movement as for the opening one. Considering only the flowers grown in Colorado Springs, we have for 15°, 20°, 25°, and 35° the closing rates of 2.3, 6, 4.6, and 1.8 for the series begun at 12 midnight; —, 11.7, 5.2, and 1.8 for the 3 A.M. series; and 5.4, 6.8, 7.1, and 7.2 for the 6 A.M. series. Although there was a general inverse ratio between the closing rates and the temperatures, there were frequent exceptions. Thus the closing rates at 15° were uniformly greater than those at 20°; and while exposure to 35° reduced the rate of closing to 1.8 for flowers exposed from midnight or 3 A.M., the rates for flowers exposed from 6 A.M. are slightly greater at 35° than at 25°. For heads from the 8300-foot habitat, at 15°, 20°, and 25° the closing rates were 8.3, 9, and 4.3 for the midnight series, thus showing values considerably above those for heads from the 6000-foot habitat at temperatures of 15° and 20°. The closing rates of *Taraxacum* heads are variable, but heads from the lower habitat subjected to temperatures between 20° and 35° beginning at midnight or 3 A.M. show an inverse relation to the temperature.

Columns 2 and 3 in Table 8 give the readings for flowers which after cutting in the field were subjected to three hours storage in a Dewar flask at 4°, darkness, and 100 per cent humidity. These flowers were comparable with those used for results given in Table 7 under the same temperature and times of starting. It will be seen that cutting and storage during the night period increased the amplitude of the response. If the rates of opening to maximum and closing to minimum are computed and compared with those given above for heads brought directly from the field to the ecostat chamber, we have 16.2 and 20 opening and −5.2 and −8.9 closing, for the unstored heads and for those kept in the field, respectively. A similar comparison of the opening and closing rates of flowers unstored and those stored for 3 hours in the Dewar flask gives 6.8 and 10.1 opening and −4.6 and −6.3 closing, respectively. This shows that the rate of movement in the flowers of *Taraxacum* is increased by cutting and storage at night; also that storage at the low and constant temperature of the Dewar flask produces a greater effect on the opening rate and a lesser one on the closing rate than storage for the same length of time under night habitat conditions.

Table 8 and Figure 9 show that the flowers of *Taraxacum* reacted to changes of temperature by opening under an increase and closing in response to a fall, and that this reaction was evident only when the periodic tendencies of the time coincided with the stimulated response. Thus flowers expanded during the morning if subjected to increased temperature, but did not do so in the afternoon. In the reverse movement a fall in temperature produced a closing reaction in the afternoon, but not in the morning.

Figure 10 indicates that the rates of movement bear a complex relation to the temperature and that the reactions can only be interpreted in the light of the periodic relations. Table 9 gives the rates of movement for the hour following the temperature change indicated at the head of the columns, and Figure 11 the increase in rate of movement in response to the temperature change. It will be seen that the movement following the rise in temperature may be either opening or closing, according to the periodic tendency of the time. Thus at 3 P.M., a rise in temperature from 15° to 20°, 15° to 25°, and 15° to 30°, resulted in the initiation or the increase of the closing movements, while similar changes earlier in the day resulted in opening movements.

Figure 11 shows that the increase in rate of movement for the hour following a temperature change of 15°, 10°, or 5°, does not bear a simple relation either to the magnitude of the stimulus, or to the temperature to which the flowers were transferred. Thus the greatest increase in opening rates was produced by a change from 15° to 20° in the midnight series, from 15° to 25° in the 3 A.M. series, and from 15° to 30° in the 6 A.M. and 3 P.M. series. The magnitude of the movement response seems to depend on a complex relation between temperature and periodicity, for the analysis of which the data here given are insufficient.

The flowers of *Taraxacum* respond to different temperature levels between 15° and 30° by an increased amplitude of expansion at the higher temperatures, but show lower degrees of expansion at 10° and 35°, which are outside the optimum range for the flowers. Flowers from mountain habitats show greater expansion at the lower temperature levels than those from the warm plains. The rate of opening to a maximum expansion varies with the temperature level between 15° and 35°, but heads from the montane region behave erratically at the higher temperature levels. The rate of opening to a maximum expansion not only varies directly with the temperature, but also inversely with the time of beginning the experiment after midnight. The rate of closing is variable, but exposure in the experimental chambers from midnight or 3 A.M. gives higher values for the montane heads than for those from the plains. After cutting, storage at night either in the habitat or at 4° constant in a Dewar flask increases the amplitude of expansion and the rate of opening and closing; storage in the Dewar flask increases the opening more and the closing less than storage in the field. Changes in temperature produce responses which result in the opening or closing of the heads according to the direction of the periodic tendency at the time the stimulus is applied; that is, periodicity determines the direction of movement. The magnitude of the increase in rate of flower movement following a sudden change in temperature is variable; it does not show a constant relation either to the degree of change, or to the temperature level to which the change is made.

EFFECTS OF LIGHT

Table 10 gives the results for heads of *Taraxacum officinale* kept under constant conditions of 25°, 50 per cent humidity, and 40 and .275 foot-candles light intensity, the light filtered through one centimeter of distilled water. The heads used were grown at Colorado Springs and were removed from the field directly to the ecostat chambers. The last six columns give the results for similar heads which had been stored 6 hours at 4°, darkness, and 100 per cent humidity before the beginning of the experiment, and were subjected to sudden changes in light intensity between 9 foot-candles (indicated by x) and darkness (indicated by y), or when in constant darkness or light of this intensity.

TABLE 10

TARAXACUM OFFICINALE

Behavior (percentage open) of flowers under constant conditions of 25°, 50% humidity, and different light intensities.

Light Conditions Time	40 ft.-c.				.275 ft.-c.				9 ft.-c. (x), or Darkness (y)					
12 mt.	3				3				$0x$	$0y$	$0x$	$0y$	$0y$	$0x$
1 a.m.	9				7				4	3	7	2	4	5
2	12				7				4	4	10	3	3	8
3	11	13			6	2			5	5	10	4	4	9
4	14	56			7	14			7	6	11	6	5	10
5	20	69			9	48			10	10	13	9	8	12
6	21	77	10		19	67	9		17	$19x$	$17y$	20	16	21
7	22	80	90		26	68	100		30	63	28	35	24	28
8	20	77	97		28	67	76		55	74	50	57	51	56
9	20	77	100	66	20	65	70	67	80	83	69	88	60	85
10	15	38	70	36	17	34	52	50	84	82	80	86	80	87
11	8	29	54	12	11	24	31	37	78	80	82	85	84	90
12 m.	3	9	48	12	8	18	21	20	56	71	50	60	$70x$	$83y$
1 p.m.	3	6	31	9	5	10	12	12	42	57	36	46	55	40
2	3	2	14	6	1	1	2	4	30	40	25	32	35	25
3	1	1	6	1	0	0	0	0	18	23	14	19	20	12
4	0	0	0	0	0	0	0	0	7	10	5	8	9	3

At the constant light intensities there was little difference in the behavior of the heads in the series begun at midnight. The amplitude of movement was low and followed the periodic rhythm. A comparison of these values with those given in Table 7 for heads under similar experimental conditions of temperature and humidity, but kept in darkness, shows that the amplitude of movement was low in the light. Thus the opening rates for 40 foot-candles, .275 foot-candles, and darkness, are 2.7, 3.1, and 6.8, respectively, and the closing rates in similar order are 2.4, 4, and 4.6. Since storage under the conditions here used has been shown to increase the sensitivity, these differences between the opening and closing rates in light and darkness would doubtless have been greater if flowers with similar storage treatment had been used.

The 3 A.M. series shows no significant difference in behavior between the light intensities for 40 foot-candles, .275 foot-candles, and darkness, the opening rates for the values given above being 16.7, 16.5, and 16.2, and the closing rates for the same intensities 8.9, 8.5, and 5.2. In the 6 A.M. series the opening rates for the light values given above were 30, 50, and 36.5, and the closing rates 14.3, 12.5, and 7.1. Here the most rapid opening occurred under a light intensity of .275 foot-candles and the highest rate of closing under that of 40 foot-candles. The 9 A.M. series showed a slightly more rapid rate of closing under light intensity of .275 foot-candles than under that of 40 foot-candles, there being no comparable series in darkness.

Under light changes between 9 foot-candles and darkness, the results of which are given in the last six columns of Table 10, there is evident an opening reaction following the light increase at 6 A.M., and a closing one following darkening at noon, but no response when the light increase took place at noon or the decrease at 6 A.M. Thus the rates of opening from 6 to 7 A.M., following the light change, are 13, 44, and 11 for constant darkness, darkness to 9 foot-candles light intensity, and 9 foot-candles light to darkness, and when this change was made at 12 noon the closing rates for these light conditions were 24, 25, and 43 respectively. It is evident that sudden changes between light intensity of 9 foot-candles and darkness produce an opening reaction to light increases and a closing one to decreases when the direction of the stimulated movement corresponds with the periodic movement at the time the stimulus is applied.

EFFECTS OF HUMIDITY

Table 11 gives the results obtained at constant conditions of 25° and darkness, with different levels of humidity. The heads of *Taraxacum officinale* were grown at Colorado Springs and received no storage before the experiments.

These readings show slightly higher expansion values at the lower humidities in all the series. Thus the midnight series expanded to a maximum of 20 at 75 per cent, and 60 at 25 per cent, and the 6 A.M. series showed 86 and 100 respectively at these humidities.

The heads placed in the ecostat at noon and the values recorded at that time bear no relation to the conditions in the experimental chambers. This inverse relation between the degree of expansion and the humidity is shown in the rates of opening and closing, which are in the order of decreasing humidities; 2.1 and 7.5 opening and 2.4 and 5.7 closing for the midnight series, 54 and 77 opening and 10.4

TABLE 11

TARAXACUM OFFICINALE

Behavior (percentage open) of flowers under constant conditions of 25° C., darkness, and 75 and 25% humidity.

Humidity %	75	25	75	25	75	25
Time						
12 mt.	3	3				
1 a.m.	3	3				
2	5	6				
3	7	10				
4	15	25				
5	15	30				
6	15	40	32	13		
7	15	50	86	100		
8	20	60	86	100		
9	20	55	72	91		
10	20	40	34	59		
11	20	30	25	55		
12 m.	15	25	12	35	87	97
1 p.m.	15	15	5	15	33	70
2	13	12	4	9	11	28
3	11	9	4	3	5	15
4	9	9	3	3	4	12
5	7	5	3	3	3	10
6	3	3	3	3	3	6

and 13.9 closing for the 6 A.M. series, and closing rates of 16.6 and 15.2 for the noon series. Under the conditions of these experiments, 25 per cent humidity tended to produce a higher maximum expansion of *Taraxacum* heads than did 75 per cent, but this difference was slight. Studies on the effects of sudden changes in humidity gave negative results in every case, showing that the values used did not produce movement reactions in the flowers of *Taraxacum*.

TISSUE STUDIES

As previously mentioned, the bracts and flowers of *Taraxacum* may be caused to exhibit movements similar to those of opening and closing, by treatment with water and various solutions of sucrose. The relation of this movement to the concentration of the solutions is the opposite of that described for tulips, the bracts and flowers of *Taraxacum* exhibiting an opening movement in water, instead of the closing characteristic of *Tulipa*. Longitudinal sections of the in-

volucral bracts and of entire flowers gave the following angles between
the tips of these organs on opposite sides of the head, the readings
being taken at 20° after 2 hours when no further movement could be
observed:

Part Used	Distilled Water	Sucrose Solutions					
		M/10	M/5	M/2	M/1	2 M	3 M
Bracts	220	195	180	130	70	0	−30
Flowers	180	176	164	146	120	86	64

The maximum opening both in bracts and flowers occurred in
distilled water, and as the concentration of sucrose was increased the
movement approached the closed position. The sections of bracts
showed a greater amplitude of movement than the entire flowers,
but the two movements varied in degree rather than in kind. Longitudinal sections through the flowers resulted in such injury to the
delicate tissues that the entire flowers were considered the better
material for study and were used throughout the work. Young
flowers, such as those used for the observations, frequently did not
open to a greater degree than the maximum obtained with distilled
water, but closed to a lower value than could be obtained even by
long treatment with a saturated sucrose solution at 20°. In fact a
4 molar sucrose solution produced no greater degree of closure than
a 3 molar, largely because during the process of closing the ligule
became rolled and in this position did not manifest further closing
movement.

It is evident that in the flowers and bracts of *Taraxacum,* as in
the perianth parts of *Tulipa,* the turgidity relations of the tissues
have an important bearing on the opening and closing movements.
Table 5 shows that the heads and floral parts active in opening and
closing slightly decreased the water content from the opening to the
closing period, but this fall was usually less than 5 per cent and was
far too low to account for the concentration of sucrose solution
required for producing the closing movement. The water and turgidity relations responsible for the movements of the flowers and
bracts were not simple, but were probably complicated by changes
in permeability of the tissues, in the irritability of the protoplasm, or
by the liberation of osmotically active substances within the cells.

As previously described, the ligule of the flower was active in
the opening and closing movements. Unlike the bracts, this organ
contains no massive tissues but is mainly composed of delicate parenchymatous cells with large, irregular, and transversely arranged
intercellular spaces. It is difficult to see how changes in the turgidity
of this tissue could result in the curvature of the floral part. In con-

trast to this, the epidermis forms a layer of compact tissue so located that a differential contraction or expansion of it on the inner and outer surfaces of the ligule could effectively produce the observed curvature, the delicate tissues beneath acting as a hinge. Since the epidermis can be quickly removed and is well suited for plasmolytic observations, and since the considerations just discussed point to the importance of this layer in the movements of the ligule, careful and extended studies were made to determine the osmotic relations between the cells on the opposing surfaces of this organ.

Small areas of epidermis were stripped from opposite surfaces of different portions of the same ligule by means of fine forceps. The freshly made sucrose solutions were checked frequently by means of the Abbé refractometer, and the temperature and illumination were kept uniform so that the values given are as strictly comparable as the plasmolytic method will permit. A solution was considered hypertonic to the tissue when the majority of the cells in two high-power fields showed incipient plasmolysis in 20 minutes, and when a similar treatment with a solution of .05 molar lower concentration showed no plasmolysis. Observations were made at 19° to 22° and are recorded as the averages of ten or more determinations. Comparative determinations were made by the use of epidermis stripped from the bracts of flowers of a single head. Tissues stripped from opposite surfaces were mounted under a single cover glass directly in the solutions recorded . The determinations were checked repeatedly on different days, with different flowers, and by different observers, and the values given here have been confirmed repeatedly. Both in flowers and bracts great variation was found in the concentration of the plasmolyzing solution for the same organ and surface, and this variation showed a gradient of increasing concentration from the base to the tip and from the median line toward the edge. Great care was exercised, therefore, to secure the tissue from equivalent regions, the areas selected being near the base, in the region of maximum curvature, and midway between the median line and the edge of the organ.

Epidermis from the involucral bracts showed no relation between the rate or direction of movement of this organ and the concentration gradient of the cells, opening or closing movements occurring when the concentration of the cell sap was high in either the outer or inner layer, or when it was equal. In the field the cells both in the outer and the inner epidermis were plasmolyzed at the time of opening by .8 molar sucrose solutions, and at the time of closing the concentration had fallen to the daily minimum of .6 molar. The maximum daily value of 1 molar was reached near midnight. These concentrations were increased by age and by 6 hours storage at 10° and at 15°, and under these conditions did not show the daily variations conspicuous in the field. Constant conditions of 30°, darkness, and 50 per cent humidity maintained values similar to those which obtained in the field at the time of opening. Concentration differences between the two surfaces were of the order of .2 molar. Since no correlation could be found between movements and epidermal concentration, work on the bracts was not pursued further. It is probable that this condition indicates the activity of tissues within the bract, rather than the insignificance of the osmotic relations between opposing layers of epidermis.

TABLE 12
TARAXACUM OFFICINALE

Osmotic relations of epidermal cells of outer and inner surfaces of the flowers when plasmolyzed with various M solutions of sucrose.

Time	Outer Surface	Inner Surface	Condition of flower
12:30 a.m.	1.95	1.30	Closed, slight opening later
2	1.80	1.60	Closed, opened later
3	1.50	1.60	Closed, opened later
4	1.50	1.70	Closed, opened later
6	1.50	1.85	Opening to 25%
8	1.10	2	Opening to 75%
9	1.60	2	Open 100%
10	1.75	1.55	Beginning to close
11	2	1.50	Closing to 75% open
12 m.	1.90	1.55	Closing to 50% open
2 p.m.	2.10	1.70	Closing to 25% open
4	1.95	1.60	Closed
6:30	2	1.60	Closed
11	2	1.30	Closed

Table 12 and Figure 12 show the daily cycle of concentrations in the epidermal cells from opposing surfaces of the ligule in the region of maximum curvature, as shown in Figure 7. Flowers from a single head were used for the determinations made on the two surfaces simultaneously; different heads of the same age were brought from the field immediately before each succeeding determination. The variability of the values is due partly to the errors of the plasmolytic method, and partly to the individual variations in the different heads. In all cases the values recorded for any one time were obtained from a single head, but different heads were used at the various hours in order to study the changes going on in the untreated flowers under field conditions. In plotting the curves in Figure 12 the individual variations thought to be insignificant in the movement cycle have been ignored and a smoothed curve drawn to show the salient changes. The curves show that the cells of the outer epidermis had a more concentrated cell sap than those of the inner at 12:30 A.M. The concentrations of the opposite sides approached and crossed near 3 A.M., diverging to a maximum difference at 8 A.M., at which time the concentration of the inner epidermal cells was more nearly equivalent to a molar sucrose solution than was that of the outer.

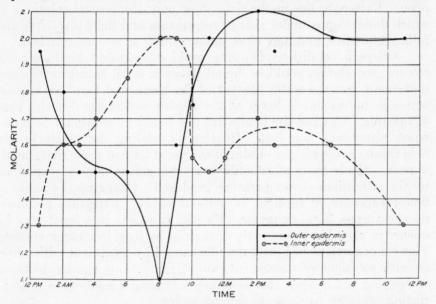

FIG. 12.—Daily march of osmotic concentrations in the outer and inner epidermis of flowers of *Taraxacum officinale*.

Opening occurred during this period, 3 A.M. to 8 A.M., and it has been shown that the rate of opening also increased in response to a temperature change of constant intensity. The concentrations again crossed near 10 A.M., and closing began at this time in the field, for at the time of this study (July) flowers in the field were closed almost completely by 2 P.M.

The osmotic concentration of the cell sap in the epidermis of the ligule goes through a daily cycle of variations, frequently forming a concentration difference between the tissue on the inner and outer surfaces. This gradient agrees in direction with flower movements, and changes in direction are quickly followed by opening or closing movements of the flower.

SUMMARY

Growth of the peduncle and duration of the life of the flower of *Taraxacum officinale* in the field vary with the season and with habitat conditions. Since the flowers open centripetally, the age of a head may be judged by the number of buds remaining at the center.

With increasing age the heads become less sensitive to stimuli, but show a greater amplitude of movement. During the early part of the flowering season and in mountain habitats, the flowers open in the morning and remain in this condition throughout the day, but during the warmer and dryer conditions of mid-summer closure occurs by noon. Factor studies in the field show only the general relations in which flowers open under rising temperature and light intensity, and falling humidity, and may close under similar or reverse relations.

Although conditions favoring rapid evaporation produce early closure, no relation could be found between floral transpiration and movement, but the water content of the heads and floral parts most active in movement is lower at the closing period than at the time of opening. Cutting the heads did not result in abnormal behavior when water was supplied. Heating or cooling the heads in the field results in opening or closing if the usual time of these movements is near. Shade tents effect only such changes as may be explained by the alterations of temperature produced. Changing the angle of flower exposure to sunlight is without effect. Irrigation produced no effect upon floral behavior. Flowers or bracts in a head may be opened or closed independently of the rest by local heating or cooling. Flowers or sections of bracts may be caused by treatment with water or with solutions of sucrose to exhibit movements similar to those of opening and closing, the movements bearing a relation to concentration opposite to those shown by tulips.

Laboratory studies showed that under constant conditions of temperature, light, and humidity, there is a periodic opening in the morning and closing in the afternoon, that this periodicity disappears within 24 hours at constant conditions and temperature levels of 20°, 25°, 30°, and 35°, but continues to the second day at 15°, and that these movements are checked at 15° or less. The reaction rates to temperature stimuli of constant intensity show periodic variations similar to those exhibited by movement of the floral parts. Heads from mountain habitats show a different temperature relation from those grown at lower altitudes. The time-temperature values for reaching maximum expansion vary with the temperature in flowers from the lower altitudes, but show maxima at both high and low temperatures in flowers from mountain habitats. At constant temperature levels the opening rates exhibited different relations in the flowers removed from the field to the experimental chambers at different times of day. Closing rates are variable and indicate habitat and field exposure differences, but in general vary inversely with the temperature. Cutting and field storage at night increase the amplitude of response and this effect upon opening is further accentuated by storage at 4°. Changes in temperature produce responses which result in the opening or closing of the head according to the direction of the periodic movement tendencies of the time, but the amplitude of response shows no close correlation with the degree of temperature change or with the temperature level to which the change is made. Constant levels of light intensity from darkness to 40 foot-candles show a slight reduction in the amplitude of movement. Sudden changes in light intensity between darkness and 9 foot-candles result in opening under increase and closing under decrease only when this movement agrees in direction with the periodic tendencies of the time. A humidity of 25 per cent favors a greater degree of floral expansion than 75 per cent.

The flowers of *Taraxacum* exhibited a daily periodicity which is not broken by stimulation such as may occur in the field, for example a change from 15° to 30°. This periodicity is predetermined by the action of one or more habitat factors several hours before floral movement, but finds expression only when such factors reach a stimulating level. Preceding workers who have studied periodicity have failed to consider the displacement which may result from temperature extremes. Results on the stimulation effects of various factors are of little value for the flowers of *Taraxacum*, unless periodicity has been checked.

Bracts and flowers may be activated to an opening movement by treatment with water. The bracts are closed by treatment with a 3 M sucrose solution at 20°, but the flowers are not completely closed by such treatment. Plasmolytic determination of the osmotic concentration of the cell sap of the epidermal cells shows no correlation between the different concentrations of the inner and outer surfaces and the opening and closing movements of the bract, emphasizing the importance of the internal tissues in floral movements. In the ligule the epidermis is particularly well suited in position and structure for producing the movements of this organ, and exhibits in the region of maximum curvature a concentration gradient parallel with the direction of flower movement, the movement being from high to low concentration.

It is significant that the level of molar concentration of sucrose solutions necessary for plasmolysis of either epidermis rises appreciably between 12 M. and 4 P.M. This may be assumed to result from several causes. Respiration may increase the osmotically active by-products between these times, buffer materials present in the cell sap may be reduced by the action of light, or translocation to floral organs may accumulate osmotically active materials. These points await clarification.

IV

ASTER BIGELOVI, ARCTOTIS GRANDIS, AND DIMORPHOTHECA AURANTIACA

ASTER BIGELOVI

FIELD BEHAVIOR

Aster bigelovi occurs commonly at Colorado Springs, reaching its best development at altitudes of 6,000 to 9,000 feet. The plants are found in open dry southern exposures and flower abundantly through August and September. The heads are 15 to 30 mm. in diameter, with deep blue rays. The flower is hemeranthous, beginning to open by 5 A.M., remaining fully expanded from 7 A.M. to 4 P.M., and closing by 6 P.M. Stages in the floral behavior are shown in Plate 4.

Of the several rows of involucral bracts which enclose the heads, all but the inner are reflexed early in the life of the bud and do not participate in the daily movements of the flower. The heads show a considerable elongation of the rays for several days before the first opening, the length increasing as much as from 6 to 10 mm. in the 4 days preceding the first opening, and this continues for 2 to 4 days after opening. The disk flowers open centripetally, the youngest and last to open being at the center of the heads. The first opening is frequently imperfect, but a portion of the rays and few or none of the disk flowers responding. During cool weather but one row of disk flower buds opens per day. These buds expand simultaneously with one or two rows of closed flowers which have been open on 1 to 3 previous days. In warm weather several rows of buds may open during a single morning and wither during the second open period. A single disk flower commonly opens on 2 to 3 successive days, the final closing being a collapse of the corolla. The rays open and close daily during the entire floral life, their opening being preceded and their closing followed by that of the inner row of involucral bracts. The rays and bracts remain active for 7 to 12 days, the activity continuing one or two days after the last disk flower has collapsed. In opening, the tips of the bracts separate and bend outward, the curvature changing throughout the length, but in greatest degree near the base. The rays follow closely on the movement of the bracts, reaching full expansion simultaneously. The disk flowers open during the time of this movement, which requires from 30 to 90 minutes.

Frequent variations appear in the field. Flowers open later in the day in the higher habitats than in the lower. The opening occurs earlier in the morning and at a lower temperature than that of

78

Flower cycle of *Aster bigelovi*

Taraxacum and *Agoseris*. Heads exposed to the morning sun and protected from cold night winds respond earlier than those less favorably situated. At the higher elevations storms which suddenly reduced the day temperature from 20° to 5° and increased a humidity of 40 per cent to saturation resulted in keeping the heads expanded throughout the night at temperatures approaching 0°. Such heads became active and moved normally when clear weather again obtained.

Field observations and experiments similar to those described in Chapter III showed the heads expanding at rising temperatures of 12.8° to 21.4°, and closing at falling temperatures of 12° to 9°. When heated to 30° in the field at 6 A.M., expansion to full opening occurred in 25 minutes. A temperature of 20° obtained in a cold bell jar did not result in closure until the normal time for this reaction. Cut flowers when placed near uncut and supplied with water opened and closed in a normal manner. The structure of the rays and bracts showed no significant difference from that described for *Taraxacum*. The movements of the rays were not altered by the removal of the inner row of bracts, nor were the movements of the undisturbed rays changed by the removal of the others from the head. The larger part of a ray may be cut away without altering the movement of the remaining basal portion.

LABORATORY EXPERIMENTS

For experiment in the ecostat chambers, heads of *Aster bigelovi* showing one or two rows of open disk flowers were used; these heads had been open on the two days preceding the experiments. The experimental methods were similar to those described in Chapter III, except that measurements of the rays were used for estimating the flower movements, and that all heads were grown at an altitude of 8000 to 9000 feet and were brought from the field immediately before the time of their installation in the experimental chambers.

PERIODICITY

Table 13 gives typical average readings of heads of *Aster bigelovi* collected at different times of day and kept under constant conditions of 2 foot-candles light intensity, 50 per cent humidity, and temperature levels of 10°, 20°, and 30°. Open flowers placed in the 10° or 20° chamber at 3 P.M. showed a periodic closing and a reopening on the following morning, but did not exhibit further movement. Open flowers placed in the experimental chamber at these temperatures during the forenoon or at noon remained open without showing periodic movements for 24 hours. Closed flowers placed in the

10° and 20° chambers during the afternoon exhibited periodic opening on the following morning, but no further movements. At 30°, open flowers remained open, showing no further movements for 40 hours. Flowers in the process of closing, when placed in the 30° chamber quickly opened and remained expanded, and closed heads rapidly became permanently expanded. At this temperature there was no evidence of periodicity. At constant temperatures of 10° and 20° periodic movements appeared only when the heads were removed from the field between noon and midnight; flowers cut during the forenoon showed no periodic activity. Evidently the periodicity is predetermined during the morning hours.

TABLE 13

ASTER BIGELOVI

Behavior (percentage open) of flowers at various constant temperatures, 2 foot-candles light intensity, and 50% humidity.

Temp. °C.	10					20					30				
Time															
3 p.m.	66					66				76					
4	51					40				81					
5	42					36				88					
6	32	7				27	5			90	3				
7	22	7				7	5			93	30				
8	17	7				6	5			94	78				
9	13	7				5	5			94	82	0			
10	10	7				4	5			96	84	23			
11	8	7				3	5			96	85	57			
12 mt.	8	7	0			5	5			96	87	75	0		
1 a.m.	10	7	0			7	5			96	88	75	45		
2	13	7	0			8	5			96	88	77	57		
3	18	7	0			17	5			96	88	77	70	0	
4	23	7	0			28	7			96	88	77	86	100	
5	35	8	0			53	12			96	88	80	97	100	
6	43	12	3	70		53	22			96	88	83	97	100	60
7	42	17	8	75		68	27			96	89	100	97	100	100
8	43	22	12	77		87	50	72		96	90	100	97	100	100
9	44	27	14	80		93	73	80		96	96	100	97	100	100
10	42	33	17	80		93	80	78		96	96	100	97	100	100
11	41	38	25	80		90	83	76		96	96	100	97	100	100
12 m.	44	47	33	80	100	86	85	76	99	96	96	100	97	100	100
1 p.m.	44	47	36	77	96	86	90	76	95	96	96	100	97	100	100
2	43	46	39	75	88	80	93	76	91	96	96	100	97	100	100
3	44	47	42	75	80	75	93	70	87	96	96	100	97	100	100
4	45	45	52	75	60	75	93	64	77	96	96	100	97	100	100
5	43	42	37	75	60	69	93	61	60	96	96	100	97	100	100
6	44	40	32	75	60	62	93	59	43	96	96	100	97	100	100
7	44	42	28	75	58	59	93	56	37	96	96	100	97	100	100
8	42	40	23	75	53	68	93	56	30	96	96	100	97	100	100
9	45	41	22	75	43	68	93	56	23	96	96	100	97	100	100
10	43	40	22	75	43	67	93	56	23	96	96	100	97	100	100
11	45	43	22	75	43	67	93	56	22	96	96	100	97	100	100
12 mt.	47	43	22	75	43	67	93	60	22	96	96	100	97	100	100

Table 14 gives the results obtained by subjecting flowers to sudden changes of temperature between 30° and 10°. This demonstrates that opening in a variable degree followed a change from 10° to 30° at periods scattered throughout the 24 hours of the day. When the changes were made at 6 P.M., 12 midnight, 2 A.M., 4 A.M., 6 A.M., and 12 M., the opening rates for the first hour following the temperature change were 28, 73, 46, 46, 62, and 54, respectively. Of these,

TABLE 14

ASTER BIGELOVI

Behavior (percentage open) of flowers in response to changes in temperature between 30° and 10°C.

x. changed from 10° to 30°.   y. changed from 30° to 10°.

Time	Changed from 10° to 30° at x						Changed from 30° to 10° at y						
12 m.	87	100			100								
1 p.m.	75	92			93								
2	63	84			84								
3	50	75		79	73								
4	42	50		61	50								
5	33	50		51	48								
6	30x	50		22	48		0						5
7	58	42	10	21	46		5	5	13	5	5	5	20
8	85	35	3	20	43		10	25	35	5	5	5	39
9	87	27	3	18	40		10	30	40	5	30	24	53
10	87	27	3	17	39		11	35	50	40	47	59	60
11	87	27	3	16	37		25	40	60	52	73	59	66
12 mt.	87	27x	4	16	36	0	68	40	60	52	73	61	73
1 a.m.	87	100	6	15	36	0	74	40	60	53	73	63	80
2	87	100	7x	15	37	0	80	41	60	53	73	65	82
3	87	100	53	25	37	0	70	41	60	54	73	65	83
4	87	100	65	35x	37	0	60	42	60	54	73	70	84
5	87	100	80	81	38	5	50	42	60	55	73	71	85
6	87	100	82	100	38x	12	56	43	60	56	73	73	85
7	87	100	89	100	100	17	63	37y	70	77	77	76	85
8	87	100	90	100	100	28	70	37	73	77	83	89	85
9	87	100	94	100	100	34	75	37	88	95	90	95	85
10	87	100	94	100	100	38	80	32	84	95	100	96	87
11	87	100	94	100	100	45	78	30	77	95	100	96	88
12 m.	87	100	94	100	100	46x	75	30	70	95	100	96	90
1 p.m.		94	100			100	75	30	70	95y	100	96	91
2		94	100			100	75	31	70	93	100	96	91
3		94	100			100	75	32	70	93	100	96	92
4		94	100			100	75	34	70	93	100y	96	92
5		94	100			100	75	36	70	93	100	96	92
6		94	100			100	75	37	70	93	100	96	92
7		94	100			100	75	37	70	93	100	93y	92
8		94	100			100	75	37	70	93	97	88	92
9		94	100			100	75	37	67	93	90	83	92
10		94	100			100	75	37	67	93	90	81	92y
11		94	100			100	75	37	67	93	90	80	92
12 mt.		94	100			100	75	37	67	93	90	80	92
							Continued unchanged						
12 mt.							75	37	67	93	90	77	92

only the first, second, and fifth are comparable, all being placed in the ecostat chambers at noon. Although the lowest opening rate following the temperature change occurred at 6 P.M., the values were too variable to establish periodicity in the flower behavior. When the temperature change was made from 30° to 10°, a slight closing movement usually followed, frequently after several hours latent period. The closing rates were extremely variable, ranging from 2 to 10 for the hour following the temperature decrease, and they did not show periodicity. Results not given in this study showed that changes between 10° and 20° differed merely in degree from those first discussed, the movement being less than that following changes between 10° and 30°.

It is evident from these studies that periodicity in *Aster bigelovi* is not as firmly fixed as in *Taraxacum*. Field conditions between midnight and noon induce a slight rhythm which is suppressed at a constant temperature of 30°, a degree seldom reached in the habitat of this species. The results obtained by subjecting flowers to sudden changes of temperature between 10° and 30° at different times of day seem to indicate that the apex of the rhythm which prepares the heads for opening is reached at about midnight.

EFFECTS OF TEMPERATURE

Table 13 shows the relation of flowers of *Aster bigelovi* to constant temperature levels of 10°, 20°, and 30°. The average values of the closely comparable series started at 6 P.M., graphed in Figure 13, indicate that the amplitude of movement varies with the temperature, the percentage maximum expansion being 47, 93, and 96 at 10°, 20°, and 30°, respectively. The maxima of the 3 P.M. series are identical, and maxima at each of the three temperatures when averaged in all cases where expansion occurred, gives 45, 93, and 98. Figure 13 shows for a single series what is evident for all, *viz.*, that the reaction time varied inversely with the temperature, and that periodic variation appeared only at the lower temperatures. If the flowers were closed, they were stimulated to open partly at 10° and fully at 20° only at the normal opening period. Although the degree of maximum expansion varied with the temperature, the flowers were not closed at 10°, showing a relation between the thermal requirements of this species and the cool mountain habitats in which it occurs.

Responses to sudden changes of temperature (Table 14) show a rapid expansion following a change from 10° to 30° at all periods tried throughout the day, and a very slight closing movement following more or less closely the reverse change. Open flowers closing in response to 10° did not reach the degree of closure at which the opening movement stopped at this temperature. Thus the percentage maximum expansion at 10° constant is 45, and in the heads changed from 30° to 10° the minimum equilibrium value is 76. Factors other

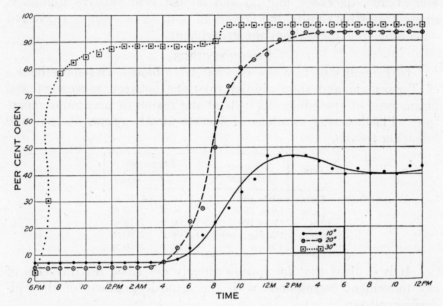

FIG. 13.—Percentage opening of flowers of *Aster bigelovi* under constant conditions of 2 foot-candles light intensity, 50 per cent relative humidity, and the temperatures indicated.

than those of temperature were operative in closing the flowers of *Aster bigelovi* in the field. The thermal requirements are evidently below those of *Taraxacum*.

EFFECTS OF LIGHT

Extensive determinations of light stimulation were not made on flowers of *Aster bigelovi* because of experimental difficulties not solved at the time this work was done. A single set of data showed that a sudden increase in light intensity from darkness to 9 foot-candles at 20° and 50 per cent humidity produced a slight opening response at 3 A.M., with an expansion from 0 to 3 per cent at 5 A.M.; further opening did not differ from that at the same temperature in darkness. A similar change in light at 6 A.M. when percentage opening had progressed to 20 resulted in expansion to 35 at 7 A.M. against 25 in darkness. Changing the flowers which had opened in the ecostat from 9 foot-candles light intensity to darkness at 3 P.M. and at 6 P.M. resulted in a slight but distinct closing movement, the flowers closing from 70 to 54 by 8 P.M. and remaining closed to the end of the experiment at 8 A.M. the following day.

EFFECTS OF HUMIDITY

A single experiment on the relation of the flowers of *Aster bigelovi* at 20°, darkness, and 25 and 90 per cent relative humidity, showed negative results, the flowers in both cases opening to 80 and remaining thus throughout the experiment.

TISSUE STUDIES

In general structure the rays of *Aster bigelovi* resemble ligules of *Taraxacum* and show similar relations between movement and plasmolysis of the epidermal cells at the region of maximum curvature. Plasmolyzing solutions of sucrose at 20° (Sept. 3) gave the following results.

Time	Flower Movement %	Epidermis	
		Inner	Outer
5 a.m.	Open 10	2.60 M	2.30 M
7 a.m.	Open 75	2.50 M	2.30 M
12 m.	Open 100	2.00 M	2.10 M
5 p.m.	Closing, open 75	2.00 M	2.20 M
7 p.m.	Closed	2.05 M	2.20 M

It is evident that for species already described the direction of ray movement corresponds with the osmotic gradient of the epidermal cell sap.

SUMMARY

Aster bigelovi attains the best flower development in mountain habitats during late summer and early fall. The heads show periodic movements only when allowed to open in the field and at temperatures below 30°. During the second day in the experimental chambers the heads remained open to a degree varying with the temperatures at which they were maintained. Temperature changes from 10° to 30° caused the opening of closed flowers, but changes in the reverse direction did not result in closure. Sudden light changes between darkness and 9 foot-candles showed a slight opening to light and closing to darkness. No effects of humidity on flower movement were observed. The osmotic concentration of the epidermal cell sap showed a difference between the inner and outer surfaces of the ligule, the gradient corresponding to the direction of floral movement.

ARCTOTIS GRANDIS
FIELD BEHAVIOR

Arctotis grandis is a common hemeranthous garden flower, the young buds of which are pendulous and closely covered by bracts with scarious tips and hairy bases. As the lavender rays elongate before opening, the bracts are forced apart and the rays cover the disk. The rays frequently reach a length of 3 cm. and show areas varying in color but darkening toward the base. The buds assume the erect position on the day preceding or the day of the first opening, which is frequently imperfect, showing but a few rays expanded and no disk flowers. During July the rays open from 7 to 9 A.M. and close by 6 P.M. on six successive days. The dark gray-blue disk buds open centripetally, one to three rows per day, exposing the black anther ring just above the tube of the corolla. The stigmas emerge at once with the stigmatic surfaces together, and toward the center of the head develop progressively longer styles carrying the closed stigma lobes with a mass of pollen high above the anthers. The stigmas expand on the second day of floral opening and this expansion occurs on three successive days before the collapse of the flower. After 6 to 7 successive openings of the rays, when all the disk flowers have expanded and the outer cycles have collapsed, the rays wither and become inactive and the involucral bracts again enclose the heads, which then become pendulous. When the seeds are matured, the heads again become erect and the bracts are reflexed to allow seed dispersal. Plate 5 shows stages in the floral behavior.

Arctotis heads do not open as early in the field, either on the day of the first and partial opening or on that of the final expansion, as they do between these ages. The plants seem well adapted to high temperatures, growing best in protected southern exposures. The behavior of cut flowers supplied with water in the field agrees with that of the uncut heads. The removal of the involucre or of a portion of the rays does not alter the behavior of the rays remaining intact.

LABORATORY EXPERIMENTS

Behavior of potted flowers used in the laboratory experimental work agreed with that of cut heads in every case.

The laboratory work was carried out by the methods already described, heads which had opened 2 or 3 days in the field being brought directly to the experimental chambers.

PERIODICITY

Table 15 shows the behavior of heads of *Arctotis grandis* under constant conditions of darkness, 50 per cent humidity, and temperature levels at 15°, 20°, 25°, and 35°. Periodic opening and closing movements were present in all cases except in the midnight series at 35°, the flowers beginning the opening movement between 5 and 7 A.M. and the closing at 11 A.M. Under constant illuminations of 40 and .275 foot-candles intensity the periodic cycle likewise appeared (Table 16), being evident in all series except the 10:30 P.M. under 40 foot-candles light. Periodicity was also evidenced in the heads of *Arctotis,* as in those of *Taraxacum,* by the nature of the reactions following a change in temperature or light.

TABLE 15

Arctotis Grandis

Behavior (percentage open) of heads under constant conditions of darkness, 50% humidity, and different temperature levels, and under sudden changes in temperature.

x. temperature change (last two columns).

Temp. °C.	15	15	15	20	20	20	25	25	25	35	35	35	15–30	15–30
Time														
12 mt.	0			5			0			3			0	0
1 a.m.	0			5			0			6			0	0
2	0			5			0			5			0	0
3	0	0		5	0		0	3		5	3		0	0
4	0	0		5	2		0	9		5	7		0	0
5	0	0		5	3		0	15		6	47		0x	0
6	0	13	1	14	65	0	34	39	4	3	57	1	50	0
6:30						18						79	67	
7	10	16	16	45	68	55	65	59	76	4	58	100	75	7
8	25	23	33	56	63	63	79	70	72	4	58	88	82	20
9	34	29	42	60	61	60	84	75	72	4	57	88	80	25
10	35	27	41	65	59	57	83	77	74	5	55	89	80	32
11	36	26	40	59	46	47	82	79	76	3	46	82	80	36
12 m.	33	21	34	56	41	40	80	71	69	2	45	77	80	36
1 p.m.	23	13	22	50	35	30	49	58	62	2	42	63	72	32
2	18	9	19	43	30	20	45	50	55	2	39	50	43	24x
2:30	12	6	16	41	25	13	41	43	47	2	37	39	38	24
3	9	6	14	32	22	12	25	30	44	2	35	38	30	20
4	6	6	12	23	20	10	10	15	41	3	33	37	18	20
5	6	5	11	21	18	9	9	13	42	3	33	33	12	19
6	1	4	16	18	17	8	12	14	44	2	32	28	12	17
7	1	4	14	18	17	7	13	14	43	2	32	28	13	18
8	2	5	12	18	18	7	14	15	42	3	33	28	12	18
9	2	3	12	18	18	6	12	15	41	3	33	28	13	18
10	1	2	13	18	18	6	10	14	41	3	33	28	13	18

Table 15 shows the results of such a change made from 15° to 30° at 5 A.M. and 2 P.M. An immediate opening response followed this change at 5 A.M., but only a slight reduction in the closing process at 2 P.M. The change from the field to the ecostat chambers at the beginning of the studies under constant conditions constitutes a stimulus of approximately similar intensity when made at midnight, 3 A.M., and 6 A.M. Table 15 shows that this stimulus produced an immediate reaction only in the 6 A.M. series at the three lower temperatures, and in the 3 A.M. and 6 A.M. series at 35°. Periodicity in the behavior of the heads of *Arctotis* appeared in similar relation when light and temperature changes were made simultaneously by transferring the heads from the field to the illuminated chambers, immediate reactions following only when the change was made at 3 or 6 A.M.

Cut heads left in the field behaved like those the averages of which are given in Tables 15 and 16. It is evident from the foregoing

Flower cycle of *Arctotis grandis*

paragraph that a period of preparation is necessary for the opening of closed flowers, and that until this is complete periodic or stimulated reactions do not occur; an increase in temperature or light which will cause opening after the preparation period will produce no such reaction during it. Since reaction follows immediately in the 3 A.M. and 6 A.M series, preparation for opening is completed in the field by this time.

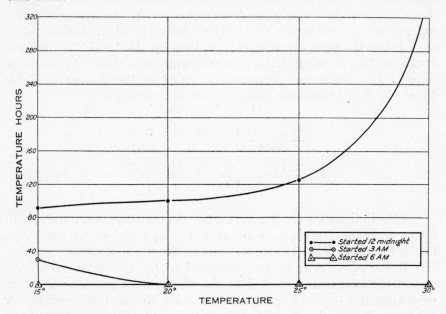

Fig. 14.—Preparation period for opening of flowers of *Arctotis grandis*.

The degree-hours of the preparation period plotted against the temperature are graphed in Figure 14; the curves show that the experimental conditions greatly modify the values, and hence the beginning of the periodic opening, the values for the midnight series increasing with temperature. At 3 A.M., preparation in the field had reached a stage at which the response to a change from the habitat (12.5°) to 15° was delayed, but it was immediate at temperatures above this. At 6 A.M., changes from the habitat (13°) to the temperature of any chamber was followed by an immediate reaction. A comparison of the values of the midnight series with those of the 6 A.M. series shows that increasing temperatures between 15° and 35° were progressively more unfavorable for the preparation period as compared to the conditions of the habitat. The degree-foot-candle-hours of the preparation period, computed from Table 16, give, for the series from 10:30 P.M. to 6 A.M., infinity, 1,200, 800, and 0 at 40 foot-candles and 35.75, 27.50, 0,

EFFECTS OF TEMPERATURE

and 0, at .275 foot-candles, indicating that high light intensity is also unfavorable for the preparation for opening.

Table 15 shows that in general the beginning of the opening reaction of the flowers of *Arctotis grandis* was hastened by higher temperatures, the average time being 5:40, 5, 5, and 2:40 A.M., for the temperatures from 15° to 35°. When the flowers were subjected to a temperature of 35° during the preparation period, the degree of opening was greatly reduced. The level of the curve of expansion values varied directly with the temperature between 15° and 25°, but was erratic at 35°, showing that this temperature was above the optimum range. The maximum percentage opening of the flowers in Table 15, at the four increasing temperatures, is as follows.

Temp. °C.	15	20	25	35
Series				
12 mt.	36	65	84	6
3 a.m.	29	68	79	58
6 a.m.	42	63	76	100

This indicates that the maximum degree of opening varied directly with the temperature between 15° and 25° in all the series, but in the range from 15° to 35° only in the 6 A.M. series.

If the opening rates are computed as the movement from the end of the preparation period to the maximum expansion, they are proportional to the temperatures between 15° and 25° except for the low value in the 6 A.M. series at 25°. The averages for all the series are 9.7, 25.3, and 34.2 for 15°, 20°, and 25°, respectively. The closing rates from the maximum to the minimum are 3.5, 4.8, and 7.9 for the same sequence of temperatures. It is evident that the opening and closing rates of the flowers vary with the temperature level.

The two final columns in Table 15 show a direct opening reaction in response to a temperature change between 15° and 30° at 5 A.M. If the opening rates following the installation of the heads in the ecostat chambers at 6 A.M. are taken for the first hour at 15°, 20°, 25°, and 35°, we have 15, 18, 72, and 78. That is, the initial rates of reaction following a sudden temperature change vary with the temperature and magnitude of the stimulus.

EFFECTS OF LIGHT

Table 16 shows the averages from heads of *Arctotis grandis* placed in the experimental chambers at 20°, 50 per cent humidity, and at constant light intensities of 40 and .275 foot-candles. The flowers under an illumination of .275 foot-candles did not react differently from those in darkness. Light of 40 foot-candles intensity reduced the degree of expansion, the maxima at this light intensity being below that at .275 foot-candles with average percentage openings of 36 and 58.

TABLE 16

ARCTOTIS GRANDIS

Behavior (percentage open) of flowers under constant conditions of 20°C., 50% humidity, and different levels of light intensity.

Light Conditions	40 Foot-candles				.275 Foot-candles			
Time								
10:30 p.m.	0				2			
11	0				2			
12 mt.	0	2			2	5		
1 a.m.	0	0			2	5		
2	0	2			2	5		
3	0	4	9		2	5	5	
4	0	8	9		2	5	7	
5	0	12	35		2	5	37	
6	0	26	48	4	7	6	48	4
7	0	20	44	63	40	25	50	66
8	0	19	44	65	50	35	49	64
9	0	18	44	68	60	48	49	63
10	0	15	39	67	60	55	46	60
11	0	14	34	62	60	55	40	54
12 m.	0	12	18	50	58	47	37	37
1 p.m.	0	9	12	41	48	43	31	27
2	0	9	10	26	41	38	27	23
3	0	9	9	11	35	32	22	19
4	0	9	9	10	22	31	21	19
5	0	9	9	9	28	29	20	19
6	0	10	9	9	26	24	19	19
7	0	10	8	9	25	24	19	19
8	0	10	8	9	25	24	19	19
9	0							

The rates of opening and closing, computed in the same way as described in the discussion on temperature effects, are as follows.

Light Conditions	40 Foot-candles		.275 Foot-candles	
Series	Opening	Closing	Opening	Closing
10:30 p.m.			14.5	13.2
12 mt.	6	2.4	10	4.4
3 a.m.	18.5	4.6	11.3	3.3
6 a.m.	21.3	21.3	62	7.9

These values are variable, due in part to the limited number of heads employed in the work, but in general show that the opening rates vary inversely and the closing directly with the light intensity.

EFFECTS OF HUMIDITY

Two experiments were performed to ascertain the effects of humidity on the behavior of flowers of *Arctotis grandis*. Constant humidity levels of 25, 50, and 80 per cent were used at a temperature of 25°. No differences in the behavior of the flowers could be detected, the rate and extent of movement and the duration of the open and closed periods being essentially the same.

TISSUE STUDIES

The rays of the flowers of *Arctotis grandis* are opened and closed by changes in curvature largely confined to a region somewhat less than a third of the distance from the base to the apex of the flower. In general structure this is similar to that of *Taraxacum,* but contains more parenchymatous tissue. Epidermis from this active region was examined by the methods described in Chapter III, and the resulting concentration curves are given in Figure 15.

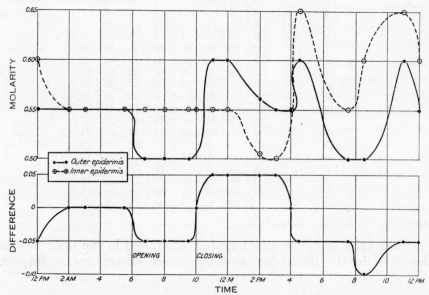

Fig. 15.—Osmotic concentrations in the outer and inner epidermal cells of flowers of *Arctotis grandis.*

The time and molarity of the sucrose solution producing plasmolysis are plotted as abscissae and ordinates in the upper curves, the solid line giving the values for the outer epidermis and the broken line those for the inner. Since different heads were used for the determinations at the various times, the parallel variations in the curves are not significant as related to flower movement, but are the result of individual and daily variations in concentration of the cell sap throughout the epidermal tissue. In order to express only the differences in concentration on the opposing surfaces, the lower curve is drawn showing equality of concentration as zero, differences favoring the outer epidermis as positive numbers, and the inner as negative ones.

The outer epidermis showed a higher concentration than the inner at midnight, and this fell to equality which persisted up to the time of the opening period. During opening, the higher concentration was found on the inner surface, and this condition changed through equality to the reverse relation during the closing period. Following this the relations were again reversed, the inner epidermis showing the higher concentration during the preparation period.

SUMMARY

It is evident from this study that there is a significant daily cycle of changes in the concentration of the cell sap in the epidermis of the flowers of *Arctotis,* which appears together with considerable field variation and a concentration gradient increasing from base to tip of ray. The direction of the concentration gradient, from high to low concentration, is never against the direction of flower movement, but the gradient which appears during the preparation period is not followed quickly by opening. Differences in concentration between the opposite surfaces do not cause the flower movements in *Arctotis,* but when such movements occur they progress from the stronger toward the weaker side and pass through a period of equal concentration on both surfaces to a reverse relation and a movement in the reverse direction. It is probable that a differential hydration of the tissues is fundamentally concerned in the movement of the rays, and that the osmotic relations of the cell sap are connected with movement through this phenomenon.

DIMORPHOTHECA AURANTIACA

FIELD BEHAVIOR

Dimorphotheca aurantiaca closely resembles *Arctotis grandis* in structure and behavior. The flowers reach their best development in Colorado Springs during late summer, at which season the yellow rays, with a length of 4 cm., expand at 6 to 7 A.M., and close in the early afternoon. The rays open and close on 7 to 8 successive days before collapse, and when old roll longitudinally 1 or 2 days before becoming inactive. The disk flowers open and close for 3 days before collapse, during which time the anthers and later the stigmas are exposed. In the field the opening and closing processes each require about 2 hours. The water content of the rays was found to be less at the closing than at the opening period, the average percentage values being 84.2 at 6 A.M. when the rays were opening, and 82.7 at 2 P.M. when the closing movement was in process.

Field studies showed that the flowers could be opened before the normal time by heating under a bell jar to 25°, and that they would close before noon under these conditions. Cooling to 18° to 20°, or irrigating the plants, produced no effect on the normal behavior. Cut heads supplied with water in the habitat behaved normally for at least 48 hours.

LABORATORY EXPERIMENTS

Laboratory studies were made by the methods already described. A marked periodicity in behavior was shown by the opening and closing of the heads under constant conditions. This periodic daily rhythm could be displaced by treatment, but appeared in the altered form under all conditions tried. Maximum opening was reached simultaneously at 15°, 20°, and 30°. Cutting was without effect on the movement. Storage at 25°, 100 per cent humidity, and darkness for 10, 13, and 16 hours before installation in the experimental chambers did not delay the time of opening when the heads were kept at 30°, 40 per cent humidity, and darkness, the maximum expansion being reached at 6 A.M. Similar storage at 35° resulted in a delay in opening so that the maximum expansion of the heads was reached 1 to 5 hours later than in the field or in the 30° chamber. Storage at 12°, 100 per cent humidity, and darkness for 10, 13, and 16 hours, which was without effect on the time of maximum expansion when the heads were placed in the 30° chamber, delayed the time at which full expansion was attained in one hour in the 25° chamber, and in 2 to 3 hours at 15°. A sudden change from 30° to 15° resulted in a slow closing movement (an hourly rate of 9.5) when carried out at 11 A.M., but a faster rate (15) at 3 P.M. Changes made from 15° to 30° resulted in immediate opening when applied at 6 A.M., but did not check closure at 4 P.M. The behavior of *Dimorphotheca* was more variable than that of *Arctotis,* possibly because of the hybrid nature of the material.

At darkness and 40 per cent humidity the percentage maximum expansion of the heads varied directly with the temperatures between 10° and 30°, being 0, 15, 55, 94, and 100, at 10°, 15°, 20°, 25°, and 30°, respectively. In the series placed in the ecostat chambers at 6 A.M. the opening rates varied with the temperature, being 1, 10, and 20, at 15°, 20°, and 30°. Under constant conditions closing was incomplete at 20° and 30°, but did not correlate closely with the temperature, being 40 to 50 at both of these temperatures. The time-temperature requirement for expansion to maximum at constant conditions of darkness and 50 per cent humidity did not differ greatly at temperature levels of 15° and 25°, but decreased as the time for periodic expansion approached, being for the 12 midnight, 3 A.M., and 6 A.M. series, 330, 225, and 180 at 15°, and 450, 225, and 125 at 25°. If these numbers are expressed in proportion to the 6 A.M. values as unity they are, in the order given, 1.83, 1.25, and 1 for 15°, and 3.60, 1.80, and 1 for 25°. It is evident that the time-temperature concept of Blackman, Livingston, and others must be modified if applied to the opening of *Dimorphotheca* heads, where there is a time-temperature-periodicity relation rather than one which is dependent only on external factors coincident with the reaction. Constant humidities of 25 and 75 per cent showed no difference in flower behavior for 24 hours. At constant levels of light of 40 and .275 foot-candles intensity the effects were similar to those described for *Arctotis*.

TISSUE STUDIES

Plasmolysis studies on the epidermis from the outer and inner surfaces of the rays showed an increasing concentration gradient from the base toward the tip and a considerable difference in concentration between the yellow and blue areas. Comparisons must be made only between areas of similar color. When the region most active in movement was considered, the direction of curvature was found to be that of decreasing concentration. In the field the concentration averages were 1.35 and 1.45 molar respectively for the outer and inner surfaces at 6:30 A.M. during the beginning of the opening process, and 1.40 and 1.30 respectively at 2 P.M. when closing was under way. When the flowers were kept closed at 15° constant temperature for 30 hours, the concentrations found were .70 and 1.10 molar for the outer and inner surfaces respectively. At 30° constant the concentrations were .80 outer, and 1 inner, and after a change to 15° at 2:30 P.M., 1.25 and .80 respectively.

In *Dimorphotheca* there is a concentration difference between the opposite epiderms in the region of active curvature similar to that found in the other flowers discussed. In preparation for the movement a difference in concentration between the opposite surfaces appears, and before the opposite movement this disappears and is reversed. It is probable that the hydration phenomena are actively concerned in the movements of the ligules of *Dimorphotheca*.

SUMMARY

The rays of *Dimorphotheca aurantiaca* exhibit a structure and behavior similar to that of *Arctotis,* displaying a daily periodicity of movement and a sensitivity to temperature and light, but no relation to humidities of the range tried. The direction of curvature of the rays during opening and closing is that of decreasing concentration in the cell sap of the epidermis. This, together with the fact that the water content of the rays is altered during the daily periods of movement, points to hydration changes in the tissues concerned.

V

TRAGOPOGON, ACROCLINIUM, AND SIMILAR FLOWERS

TRAGOPOGON

FIELD BEHAVIOR

Two species of *Tragopogon* are common in waste places at Colorado Springs; *T. pratensis* with yellow flowers, and *T. porrifolius* with purple. The flowers are hemeranthous, like those discussed in the preceding chapters, but close early in the day, the open period during July being 10 to 11 A.M. The opening and closing movements are each completed in the field in about 45 minutes. Like *Taraxacum*, the heads may remain open throughout the day in shaded habitats. In opening, the involucre spreads first at the tip, the flexion extending toward the base until the bracts are spread to an angle of about 45°; the first opening may stop at this stage. During the opening of the bracts the rays bend out and unroll, reaching full expansion simultaneously with the involucre. The disk flowers open after the bracts and rays have expanded, the opening progressing centripetally and frequently not beginning until the second opening period of the head. The movements of the rays and bracts are largely the result of curvature in a limited region near the basal end. The bracts, being thick and bent in from the midrib, seem to open less readily than the rays which are usually closely applied against the inner surface during the opening movement and limit the degree of expansion of the rays. Very young heads do not open to as great a degree as do the older ones, but the final opening is often partial, like the first. Several stages in the opening of the heads of *T. porrifolius* are shown in Plate 6.

Twenty buds of *Tragopogon porrifolius* were numbered on plants growing in a dry level meadow, and twenty buds of *T. pratensis* found on a dry western slope partly protected by small trees, as well as ten of the latter species growing in an irrigated meadow. These heads were observed daily during the opening period, and results are shown in the following table, the first column under each species observed listing the number of heads which showed the behavior given in the second column of the table, the percentages being computed from these values.

In both species the involucre opens 1 to 4 times, most commonly 3. The rays and disks of *T. porrifolius* open once or twice, but in *T. pratensis* three openings are not uncommon. The disk flowers of both species usually open but once, the successive opening given in the table being due to buds which did not open on the first expansion of the bracts and rays.

Opening Movements		T. porrifolius		T. pratensis		T. pratensis (irrigated)	
		No.	%	No.	%	No.	%
1	Involucre openings	1	5	3	15	1	10
2	Involucre openings	6	30	8	40	3	30
3	Involucre openings	9	45	9	45	5	50
4	Involucre openings	4	20	0	0	1	10
1	Openings of rays	7	35	7	35	0	0
2	Openings of rays	13	65	11	55	8	80
3	Openings of rays	0	0	2	10	2	20
1	Openings of disks	7	35	7	35	2	20
2	Openings of disks	13	65	11	55	5	50
3	Openings of disks	0	0	2	10	3	30

Factor readings were made in the field at the time of the flower movement and found to be variable. The following are typical, the readings being made in close proximity to several flowers in the process of movement. Light intensity is given as percentage sunlight, measured by solio paper.

Opening			Closing		
Temp. °C.	Humidity %	Light %	Temp. °C.	Humidity %	Light %
9.5	58.3	5.8	31.5	35.5	60
11	95	2.5	23	74.5	80
9.5	48.5	33	31.5	26	80
7.5	78	33	22	39	80
8.8	72	15.5	29.3	27	80
10.1	66	7.8	31.5	24	80

In general the flowers open at periods of low but rising temperature and light, and high but falling humidity; but in view of the great variation in the values of the three factors measured at the time of opening and closing on successive days, and of the probability of a delay between stimulus and response, little more can be safely concluded from the readings.

Transpiration studies of *Tragopogon* were inconclusive, any effects of the flower position being obscured by the variation of individual heads. The percentage water content of ten heads of equal age averaged 85.1 when first open at 6 A.M.; an equal number of heads gave an average of 82.2 at 11 A.M. when the closing movement was in progress, the individual variations between the heads being about 1 per cent.

Plate 6

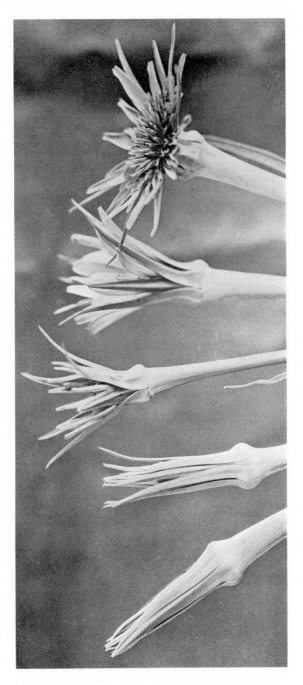

Flower cycle of *Tragopogon porrifolius*

EXPERIMENTAL BEHAVIOR AND FLORAL STRUCTURE

Undisturbed closed heads of both species were opened at 3 A.M. by heating to 30° in a bell jar with humidity at 60 per cent, but closed heads did not open under similar treatment during the afternoon. Normal open heads were closed at 9:30 A.M. by heating from 30° to 32°, at 28 per cent humidity.

In heads cut from the plant immediately before the opening period, no movements occurred for over 24 hours; that is, the heads did not expand the first morning after cutting. Following this period the heads behaved normally for 48 hours or more if placed in the habitat. Heads removed while open, the cutting in all cases being done under water, remained expanded for the normal priod, closing and reopening with the undisturbed heads in the same locality. Heads cut after closure would frequently but not invariably begin normal movement on the following morning. Apparently a period of adjustment or recovery is necessary after cutting before normal opening occurs, but this is not the case for the closing movement. Cutting the heads with varying lengths of peduncle made no change in the flower behavior. Closed heads cut immediately before the opening period could not be stimulated to open by a sudden increase in temperature to 35°, but if placed in a bell jar within which the air was kept saturated, the heads opened and continued their normal behavior.

A typical experiment was carried out July 8. Ten closed heads of *T. pratensis* which had been fully expanded for the first time on the preceding day, were cut at 5 A.M. and half the number placed in each of two bell jars on slate bases in the field. The air in one jar was kept at approximately 98 per cent humidity, and the other at 20 per cent. The temperature and light intensity varied in the sequence of these conditions outside, the former rising to 40°, and the latter remaining approximately 70 per cent of the field value. At 7 A.M. the heads in the humid bell jar were fully expanded, as were the undisturbed ones nearby; but those in the dry bell jar were still closed. At 10 A.M. the normal heads were closed, the cut heads in the dry atmosphere had not opened, and those in the moist jar were still fully expanded, remaining in this condition until 4 P.M. The following morning all heads opened at 6:10 A.M., the degree of expansion being less for the heads in the dry bell jar than for those in the moist one.

The opening of *Tragopogon* flowers is apparently intimately connected with turgidity and water relations when these are made a limiting factor by cutting the heads, since normal heads enclosed in a moist chamber do not alter their behavior.

Removal of the leaves from a plant produced no effect on the flower movement in *T. pratensis*. Removal of the disk flowers while the heads were expanded produced immediate and permanent closing of the involucre in both species. This closure took place in one to two minutes, much faster than the normal movements, and was probably due to the partial collapse of the receptacle. The removal of the involucre bracts produced little or no effect on the opening or closing of the ray and disk flowers, the rays rolling and turning toward the center just as in the normal inflorescence.

The structure of the ligule and bract in cross section is shown in Figure 16. The ligule is composed of loosely arranged tissue, and the epidermal layers alone are suited in structure and position for producing curvature in the ligule by differential elongation. The outer epidermis is more highly cuticularized than the inner and contains stomata which appear inactive. It appears that the only tissue forming a continuous layer so situated as to produce curvature is the epidermis, since the vascular bundles of the corolla are not distributed throughout but are located centrally where differential expansion would not be likely to produce movement. The ligules of *Tragopogon* exhibit considerable movement, since they not only bend in and out, largely as the result of curvature in a limited region, but also roll longitudinally. In these movements the epidermal layers probably play an important rôle. The difference in the cuticularization on the two surfaces helps to explain the peculiar behavior of the ligules when the water supply is reduced by the cutting of the flower. Transpiration might be expected to take place more rapidly from the inner surface than from the outer, resulting in a differential turgidity productive of a closing movement. Oiling the surface of the ligules was tried with a view to proving this point, but it was found that the results were doubtful because the oiled surfaces prevented normal movement, and in closing the oil became irregularly distributed over both surfaces.

The structure of the involucral bracts shows important differences (Fig. 16). The epidermal layers do not differ greatly in cuticularization, but the outer layer is heavily underlaid with collenchyma. This more massive structure would not be so easily curved, and it is doubtful whether a tissue layer such as the epidermis could effectively accomplish it. It is more probable that other tissues are instrumental in producing the movements of the bracts, and that the epidermis is of importance in the control of transpiration and hence of turgidity.

LABORATORY EXPERIMENTS

Little work was done on *Tragopogon* in the laboratory, because the potted material proved unsatisfactory, and cut heads were found erratic in behavior unless taken from the field in the open condition or left for 24 hours after cutting. *Tragopogon* is a flower for which the

results of the most detailed laboratory experiments may be in error unless checked by field studies. The average percentage openings

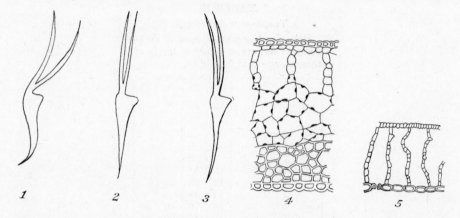

FIG. 16.—Longitudinal sections through the involucre and receptacle of *Tragopogon pratensis.*

1—after removal of the cuticle and treatment for 15 minutes at 20° with distilled water; 2—the same section after 15 minutes at 20° in molar sucrose solution; 3, after an additional immersion of 2 hours in saturated sucrose solution at 20°; 4, cross section of involcural bract in the region of maximum curvature; 5, cross section of the corolla in the region of most active curvature.

given in Table 17 have been computed from results for heads which seemed to behave normally under experimental conditions. All the heads used had opened for the first time on the day preceding the experiments, were cut immediately before being placed in the experimental chambers, and opened completely and normally when placed in the field on the day following the experiments here recorded.

Table 17 shows that these results confirm those obtained in the field. When cut in the closed condition at midnight, the heads opened slightly at 25 per cent humidity, and to nearly full expansion at 75 per cent. When the heads were cut in the opening condition at 6 A.M. the opening process continued to completion at 20° but was limited at 35°, indicating that the latter temperature was above the optimum. Permanent injury did not result from the low humidity or high temperature, since the heads all behaved normally when placed in the field the following day. The periodic behavior is evident from the fact that the flowers opened and closed only at the time normal for these reactions in the field. The effect of the time of cutting also shows the periodic nature of the flower movement. The opening rates, taken from Table 17 in the order given, are 1.3, 10.3, 50, and 9, and the closing rates in the same order are 2.4, 20.8, 16, and 13.6. The opening and closing movements were of greater magnitude at 75 per cent humidity than at 25 per cent in the material cut at midnight, and greater at 20° than at 35° in the 6 A.M. series.

TABLE 17

TRAGOPOGON PRATENSIS

Behavior (percentage open in darkness) of flowers at different levels of temperature and humidity.

Temp. °C.	25	25	20	35
Humidity %	25	75	50	50
Time				
12 mt.	8	8		
1 a.m.	8	8		
2	8	9		
3	9	11		
4	13	28		
5	13	45		
6	16	70	50	50
7	16	87	100	64
8	19	90	68	68
9	18	50	66	57
10	17	19	56	25
11	9	11	29	7
12 m.	8	7	7	1
1 p.m.	7	7	4	0
2	7	7	4	0
3	7	7	4	0

Entire bracts of *T. porrifolius* and *T. pratensis* exhibit slight movements similar to those of opening, when treated for two hours at 20° with saturated sucrose solution. This opening movement is not complete after prolonged treatment, but a closing movement readily results from treatment with distilled water. Figure 16 shows the positions of two bracts when treated with water and with sucrose solution. A longitudinal section of a bract was more easily affected by this treatment, but did not show much curvature either in distilled water or saturated sucrose solution, unless the cuticle had been removed by scraping the surface lightly. If the cuticle was thus removed from the inner surface, distilled water produced an opening movement, and .5 M sucrose solution a closing response, in 15 minutes at 20°; if the outer cuticle was removed, the action was the opposite, distilled water causing a closing movement and sucrose solution an opening. For complete closing, molar solutions were required. This indicates that a differential turgidity on the two surfaces of the bract may produce the movements of opening and closing and that the direction of this movement is dependent on the permeability and rate of entrance of water on the two surfaces. Probably the differential permeability of the underlying tissues is of importance in this phenomenon.

The ligules are affected much more readily than the bracts. When expanded they may be rolled, as in closure, by treatment with .1 M sucrose solution at 20°, and reopened by treatment with water. The curvature is similarly affected; that is, opening movements are produced by distilled water, and closing by sucrose solutions, but this action does not occur as readily or completely as the rolling movements. The ligule is completely rolled by .1 M sucrose solution in 15 minutes at 20°, but there is little curvature even in stronger solutions. Opening occurs in water in the same length of time.

Plasmolysis studies on the opposing epidermis in the regions most active in movement indicated that a daily cycle of concentration occurred similar to that in *Taraxacum*. The results obtained are graphed in Figure 17, in which the molar concentration of sucrose solution producing incipient plasmolysis is plotted against time. The values for the bracts differ but little at any period during the day, but are greater in the cells of the inner epidermis before and during the opening and open periods, and become higher in the outer layer only during a short period at the beginning of closing. Between the opposite epiderms in the bracts there was no significant difference in concentration during the closed period except immediately before opening.

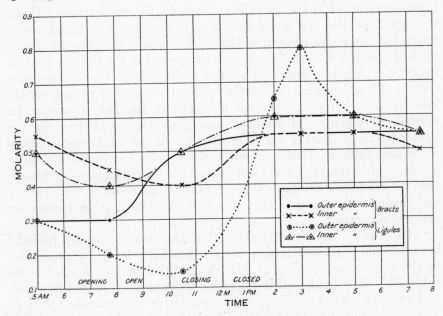

Fig. 17.—Concentrations of sucrose solutions causing incipient plasmolysis in the cells of the opposing epidermis on the bracts and ligules of *Tragopogon pratensis*.

The ligules exhibited a somewhat similar relation, but the differences between the two epiderms were greater than those that occurred in the bracts. From early morning until after 10:30 A.M. (no determinations were made between this time and 2 P.M.) the concentration in the inner epidermis was greater than that in the outer. This included the opening and open periods and the beginning of the closing. During the early part of the closed period the concentration of the outer epidermal cells reached the maximum. The plasmolytic results indicate that the difference in concentration between the opposite epidermal layers is never as great in the bracts as in the ligules, and this agrees with the observations that a more concentrated solution is required for producing the closing movement in the flowers than in the bracts. Changes in the concentration probably accompany those of hydration, and both are closely connected with floral movements.

SUMMARY

The flowers of *Tragopogon pratensis* and *T. porrifolius* are hemeranthous, opening early in the morning and closing during the forenoon, but displaying a very variable behavior. Although both opening and closing take place under conditions of rising temperature and light intensity and falling humidity, closing occurs under conditions which promote an increasing rate of transpiration, and an intensification of these conditions hastens the movement. Floral transpiration does not show variations correlated with floral movement, but the water content of the head is less at the time of closing than of opening. Closed flowers may be opened in the field by heating to 30°, but only at a time near that at which this movement normally occurs. Closed heads cut shortly before the opening period remain inactive for 24 hours, and then if placed in the field continue the normal movements. If removed immediately after closing, the behavior on the following day is erratic, but if cut while open normal movement follows. Heads cut while closed behave normally if kept in a humid atmosphere. The structure of the ligule makes it probable that the epidermis produces the curvatures that result in the opening and closing movements of this organ; in the bracts other tissues are actively concerned.

Laboratory experiments show that the flowers display periodic behavior and react to temperature and humidity levels by expanding to the maximum opening at high humidities and at temperatures below 35°. The ligules exhibit opening movements if placed in water, and may be closed again by treatment with .5M sucrose solution. The bracts do not respond as readily, but show a similar action that may be greatly accelerated by removing the cuticle of the inner surface, and reversed by the destruction of the outer. It is evident that turgidity relations in the active regions of the floral parts are of great importance, and that alterations in the rate of water conduction or in foliar transpiration affect floral movement through this condition.

CREPIS ALPINA AND RELATED FLOWERS

The behavior of *Crepis alpina, C. tectorum, C. foetida, C. runcinata, Hieracium sabaudum, H. saxifragum*, and *H. boreale* was essentially similar, and these flowers are not distinguished in the following discussion. Field work was carried out on all species, but the laboratory study was confined to *C. alpina* and *C. foetida*. The opening of the heads was similar to that described for *Arctotis*, differing in that the stigma lobes showed more movement, the filaments bending centripetally as the flowers closed, and forming a network above the surface of the closing heads. At Colorado Springs, opening occurred at 7 to 10 A.M., and closing at 1 to 4 P.M. The heads opened on 5 or 6 successive days, after which the bracts remained closed until the final opening when the fruit matured. The floral behavior of *Crepis runcinata* is shown in Plate 7. The individual flowers of the heads opened on 3 successive days before collapsing. As in the case of *Tragopogon,* conditions favoring a high rate of foliar transpiration shortened both the length and the number of open periods, and the water content of flowers was found to be 3 to 4 per cent less at the time of closing than at the opening period. Flowers in the field responded to an increase in temperature from 13.4° to 30° by expanding when this change was made shortly before the usual time of opening in the field, but exhibited no movement when this was applied after the normal closure at 3 P.M. Cut flowers were more erratic than uncut, but usually opened and closed normally.

PERIODICITY AND TEMPERATURE RELATIONS

Since *Crepis alpina* was not available at the laboratory, it was cut 3 hours before the first experiment and stored in a thermostat at 10°, darkness, and 100 per cent humidity, being thus brought to the laboratory and removed immediately before installation in the ecostat. The general behavior was similar to that of *Taraxacum,* storage increasing the amplitude of response rather than the nature of the movement. Heads became inactive after storage for 48 hours or more. Experimental methods were otherwise similar to those described.

This shows an opening reaction the extent of which varied with the temperature at 10°, 15°, and 20°, but did not increase at 30°, which is apparently super-optimal. Complete opening did not occur before 5 A.M. in any case, and the beginning of the opening movements was never observed before midnight. No movement followed installation in the 10° or 15° chambers before 3 A.M. The slight opening reaction observed at 10° was probably due to the stimulus resulting from the transfer of the heads from the thermostat chamber through the laboratory temperature to the ecostat, as no opening occurred when the flowers remained in the thermostat at 10°. At 15° the extent of expansion, when this occurred, varied with the time of placing in the experimental chambers; and this relation also held for 20° and 30°, up to the 9 A.M. installation which fell below those of 3 and 6 A.M. At 20° and 30° the rate of opening varied directly with the time of installation up to 9 A.M. The preparation period decreased in all cases as the time of periodic expansion was approached; that is, the result of the change from the thermostat to the 20° and 30° chambers followed immediately at 3 A.M. and later, and to the 10° and 15° chambers at 6 A.M. and 9 A.M. In the 9 P.M. series, sudden changes in the temperature from 15° to 30° resulted in immediate opening when made at 6 A.M., the rate for the hour following the change being 80. In a similar change from 15° to 20° the rate was 55, but when these changes were made in the opposite direction at 6 A.M. no movement followed.

CREPIS ALPINA
Behavior of heads under constant conditions of darkness, 50% humidity, and the temperatures given.
1. Percentage maximum opening.
2. Hourly rate of opening.
3. Number of hours preparation period in experiment chambers.

Temp. °C.	10			15			20			30		
Time	1	2	3	1	2	3	1	2	3	1	2	3
9 p.m.	0			0			40	5	5	50	10	5
12 mt.	0			0			75	9	2	75	25	2
3 a.m.	0			55	9	1	100	33	0	100	33	0
6	5	3	0	70	8	0	100	50	0	100	100	0
9	5	3	0	73	10	0	75	37	0	60	60	0

SUMMARY

Various species of *Crepis* and closely related forms behave much like *Taraxacum*, the flowers opening under constant conditions or in response to a rise in temperature only near the time of the normal daily expansion in the field.

REICHARDIA TINGITANA

Reichardia was grown in the garden at Colorado Springs, reaching the best development in July when this study was made. The field behavior was very similar to that of *Arctotis*. The floral life history is shown in Plate 8. The flowers and bracts opened and closed 7 to 8 successive days, the open period being from 7 to 8 A.M. to

Flower cycle of *Crepis runcinata*

11 A.M. At the time of closing, the water content of the flowers averaged 4 per cent below that found at opening. Cutting produced no abnormal behavior for 24 hours. All experimental work was carried out on freshly cut material which had made two daily openings before the time of cutting. The behavior of the heads was studied under constant conditions of darkness and 50 per cent humidity, and at temperature levels of 20° and 35°; also at 20° and 50 per cent humidity under illuminations of 40 and .275 foot-candles light intensity. In all cases, opening and closing occurred in the usual daily rhythm, changing in degree under the various experimental conditions. In darkness the rate and degree of opening were greater at the lower temperature in the midnight and 3 A.M. series, but varied directly with the temperature in the 6 A.M. series, showing, as in *Taraxacum,* that low temperatures are favorable for the preparation for opening, and higher temperatures for the opening process itself. At .275 foot-candles light intensity, expansion was greater than in darkness or under illumination of 40 foot-candles in the midnight and 3 A.M. series, but in the 6 A.M. series the greater expansion occurred under the more intense illumination. The time at which the maximum opening occurred was earlier at 35° than at 20°, but was not affected by the light differences.

Reichardia exhibited a behavior in the field and under constant experimental conditions similar to that of *Taraxacum.* The preparation for opening is favored by darkness and low temperatures, and the rate and amplitude of movement vary directly with the temperature when the preparation has been completed.

OTHER HEMERANTHOUS COMPOSITAE

Field studies of *Agoseris californica, A. grandiflora, A. major, Cichorium intybus, Lactuca pulchella, Layia elegans, Malacothrix californica, M. fendleri, Ptiloria tenuifolia, Rhagadiolus edulis, Sonchus arvensis,* and *Tolpis barbata,* showed a floral behavior essentially similar to that of *Taraxacum, Crepis,* and *Reichardia.* There are numerous differences in the floral life histories, some of which are shown in Plate 9 of *Cichorium,* Plate 10 of *Layia,* and Plate 11 of *Ptiloria.* The buds of *Layia* do not close completely and the bracts take no part in the closure. During the active life of the heads the rays continue growth and movement, opening early in the forenoon, and closing in the afternoon to an erect position and continuing to elongate (Plate 10). The receptacle gradually assumes a conical form, bringing the younger flowers near the center of the head to an elevated position and maintaining the fruits thus until distribution. *Ptiloria* differs from the types of composites described, in displaying flower movements in heads containing but five flowers. All the flowers of the head expand simultaneously in the early forenoon, and close several hours later in the day, repeating this behavior on 2 to 3 successive days. In opening, the flowers curve in a region nearly midway between the base and the tip, the involucral bracts opening but slightly. On the collapse of the corollas the bracts close, and reopen to allow the distribution of the fruits. *Rhagadiolus* shows an interesting modification of movement; after 5 to 7 daily opening and closing movements, the bracts curve longitudinally, enclosing the withering corolla and developing fruit.

Detailed experimental studies in the laboratory were not undertaken on these species, but such studies as were made indicated that the flowers react much as in the forms already described. Periodicity and an opening response to sudden increases in temperature were characteristic of all. A decrease in water content of the floral parts occurred in all species during the open period, and the turgidity conditions of the tissues seemed similar to those already discussed.

ACROCLINIUM ROSEUM

The buds of *Acroclinium* are supported in a pendulous position by the long slender peduncles until one or two days before the first opening of the flowers, when the heads become erect. The bracts are first reflexed on bright summer days at 6 to 10 A.M., and close at 4 to 5 P.M. The opening movement is somewhat slower in the field than the closing, but each is completed in one hour or less, and is repeated on 10 to 15 successive days. The heads close rapidly with the coming of rain, the process at times being completed in less than 10 minutes. No close correlation between the opening and closing movements and the temperature could be established in the field, the heads expanding with a rising temperature and falling humidity, and closing when these factors change in the reverse order, as in other hemeranthous forms. When approaching the end of the period of floral activity, the bracts go through a decreased amplitude of movement and finally remain in the reflexed position, the receptacle becoming conical. Typical stages in the life history are shown in Plate 12.

Cut flowers behaved normally for several days when exposed in the field, showing a sequence and rate of movement similar to that of uncut material. Both cut flowers and heads growing on potted plants were used for the laboratory studies and uniformly gave similar results. Determinations of the water content of the basal portion of the bracts showed a fall of approximately 5 per cent from the opening to the closing period.

The scarious rays of *Acroclinium* are composed largely of dead cells with transparent walls and gas-filled interiors. Near the base

Flower cycle of *Reichardia tingitana*

of the rays this transparent tissue abruptly gives way to living chlorenchyma, the junction being the point of maximum curvature in the opening and closing movements. When the cells of this tissue are killed by drying at atmospheric temperatures, by heating to 100°, or by age, the movements may still occur. Brief treatments with chloroform vapor temporarily decrease the amplitude of movement, the heads remaining partly closed. This effect may be imbibitional. Individual rays cemented to a glass slide by means of gum arabic solution exhibit an opening and closing movement when the air about them is heated or cooled. Since this procedure alters both temperature and humidity, no conclusions concerning the causative factors could be drawn. When the temperature is maintained constant at 20° and the bracts are treated with air saturated with water vapor, closing movements occur. Bracts treated with chloroform vapor for two hours closed, reopened on exposure to the air, and could not be again stimulated to movement by treatment with water vapor. Since closing movements took place in the detached bracts, the receptacle and outer parts of the involucre seem to act merely as a support for the moving organs of the head and not to be intimately concerned in the movements.

LABORATORY EXPERIMENTS

Laboratory studies were carried on by the same methods as described for the other species previously considered. The heads showed no opening and closing responses correlated with constant temperatures of 15° and 30°, and did not show movement in response to sudden changes between these levels. No effect of light intensities between darkness and 40 foot-candles could be observed. The heads readily responded to changes in humidity. The behavior of heads kept under constant conditions of 25° and darkness, and at constant humidities of 25 and 75 per cent, and sudden changes between these values, is graphed in Figure 18.

The curves show that the heads, after coming into equilibrium with the experimental conditions, remained at a constant degree of opening inversely proportional to the humidity throughout the course of the experiment. Reciprocal changes made at intervals throughout the day were followed immediately by movements showing the same relation to the humidities in which the heads were placed. The curves of the heads under constant conditions revealed no periodic variation, and the response to changes in humidity between 25 and 75 per cent were followed immediately by movements similar in rate and degree at different times of day. Thus the closing rates for the two-hour periods were 38, 46, 47, 46, 45, 46, for one series; and 41, 39, 39, 38, 37, for the reciprocal series; and the opening rates for the two series were 41, 47, 46, 45, 46, and 39, 37, 38, 37, 38, 37.

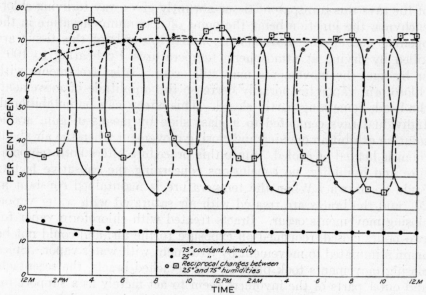

Fig. 18.—Behavior of *Acroclinium roseum* under constant conditions of temperature and light, and at different constant and variable humidities.

EFFECTS OF HUMIDITY

The degree of opening at 25 per cent humidity was 71, and at 75 per cent humidity was 13; that is, the curve of floral movement is steeper than that of humidity, the relation being 3 to 5.5. The heads transferred from the laboratory to the 25 per cent humidity chamber opened to a degree from which there was a temporary fall before the final rise to the equilibrium value (Fig. 18), because this value is thought to have resulted from an unequal water loss from the two surfaces and a temporary reversal by conduction from adjacent tissue or from the contraction of the structure as a whole, as has been shown by Rywosch (1925). This characteristic of the reaction appears in the greater degree of opening in the heads changed to 25 per cent humidity than in constant equilibrium value at this level. The fact that the curves do not reach the 75 per cent level indicates that the intervals in the chamber at this humidity were insufficient to allow equilibrium. Reference to the 75 per cent constant curve shows that 6 hours were required for reaching final equilibrium.

In order to study the rates at which equilibrium was attained under various conditions, readings were made as frequently as movement could be accurately determined. The data thus obtained are given in Table 18, in which opening and closing movements are recorded as observed. The opening movement continued to approxi-

Flower cycle of *Cichorium intybus*

TABLE 18

ACROCLINIUM ROSEUM

Behavior (per cent open) of heads subjected to various temperatures and humidities.

OPENING

9% H., 15 °C.		14% H., 17 °C.		15% H., 16 °C.		16% H., 30 °C.		18% H., 25 °C.		32% H., 17 °C.		56% H., 30 °C.		59% H., 18 °C.		63% H., 17 °C.		82% H., 15 °C.	
Hours	% Open	Hours	% Open	Hours	% Open	Hours	% Open	Hours	% Open	Hours	% Open	Hours	% Open	Hours	% Open	Hours	% Open	Hours	% Open
0	0	0	0	0	0	0	0	0	0	0	0	0	0	0	0	0	0	0	0
0.03	5	0.02	5	0.03	5	0.21	5	0.14	5	0.02	2	0.21	0	0.03	5	0.02	2	0.02	0
0.12	70	0.08	50	0.13	50	0.38	80	0.24	77	0.23	25	0.63	0	0.16	6	0.50	4	0.26	0
0.27	90	0.15	75	0.20	75	0.62	100	0.51	92	0.43	46	1.13	0	0.50	6	1	5	0.62	0
0.62	98	0.28	85	0.37	90			1.10	100	1	85								
		0.34	93																

CLOSING

100% H., 30 °C.		13% H., 17 °C.		30% H., 17 °C.		43% H., 18 °C.		56% H., 18 °C.		59% H., 18 °C.		63% H., 17 °C.		88% H., 17 °C.	
Hours	% Open	Hours	% Open	Hours	% Open	Hours	% Open	Hours	% Open	Hours	% Open	Hours	% Open	Hours	% Open
0	100	0	100	0	100	0	100	0	100	0	100	0	100	0	100
0.01	95	0.03	95	0.12	95	0.08	95	0.03	95	0.03	95	0.02	95	0.02	95
0.12	20	0.50	95	0.53	95	0.13	95	0.16	85	0.16	75	0.16	75	0.06	75
0.58	0					0.50	95	0.50	75	0.50	75	0.50	75	0.12	50
														0.22	25
														0.50	5

mate completion at humidities below 20 per cent, and little or no expansion took place at humidities of 50 per cent or more.

Three typical opening curves are shown in Figure 19. It will be seen that the curves are sigmoid at the lower humidities, flattening as the humidity was increased. Hygroscopic curves of organic materials do not commonly assume this form, but continue at an increasing rate with higher humidity values (International Critical Tables, vol. 2.) If the difference between two materials of unequal hygroscopicity is taken, the resulting curves more nearly approach the form found for *Acroclinium*. The difference between the values for newspaper and kraft wrapping paper is flattened in Figure 20 for comparison. Although the values for this curve are weights instead of curvature, as recorded for *Acroclinium*, the forms are similar. The movements of the floral parts are evidently the result of unequal rates of expansion of two opposing layers. The maxima readings are not necessarily equilibrium values, as the time of observation was often insufficient to reach this point.

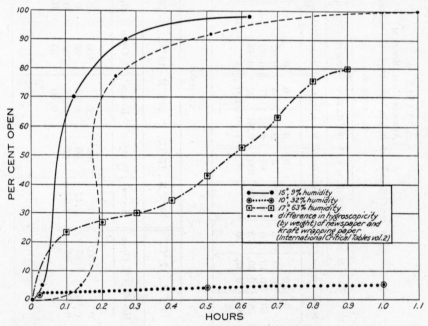

Fig. 19.—Percentage opening of flowers of *Acroclinium roseum* under different conditions of temperature and humidity.

The hourly rates of opening to maximum may be computed from the data in Table 18, and these plotted merely against the vapor pressures of water at the given temperatures and humidities as shown in Figure 20. The expansion curve is similar to that of the expansion

Flower cycle of *Layia elegans*

of the swelling of gelatin as given by MacDougal (1920), approaching the axes asymptotically. The single divergent point was probably due to individual variation in the heads employed.

The closing process followed curves of similar form (Table 18). The living epidermis over the chlorenchyma at the point of maximum movement showed a gradient of osmotic concentration as determined by plasmolysis. In an open head the solutions of sucrose isotonic with the outer and inner epidermis were 0.3 M and 0.4 M respectively. In the closed head the corresponding values were 0.3 M and 0.2 M.

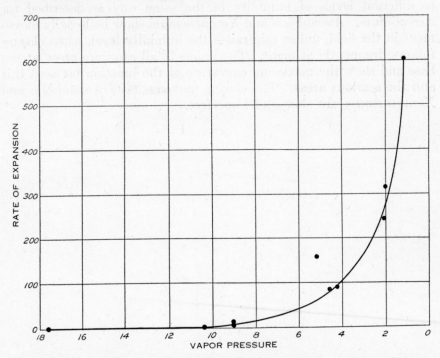

Fig. 20.—Hourly rates of expansion to the observed maximum of flowers of *Acroclinium roseum* at various vapor pressures.

SUMMARY

The heads of *Acroclinium roseum* show a daily opening and closing movement, closure occurring in the evening or before a rain. Heads are but slightly affected by temperature or light changes, but are very sensitive to humidity, the positions varying inversely with the vapor pressure. The rate of opening follows the swelling curve of colloids and seems to result from the unequal turgidity of opposed tissue layers. The bracts that show movement are largely composed of scarious tissue, but the curvature (resulting in movement) occurs chiefly in the region where this tissue and living chlorenchyma meet. Movements are not prevented by treatment that kills the living cells of the chlorenchyma, and are probably due to the hygroscopicity of the cell walls.

SPECIES SIMILAR TO ACROCLINIUM

Ammobium, Helichrysum, Rhodanthe, and *Xeranthemum* exhibit floral behavior differing from that of *Acroclinium* largely in degree of movement. *Helichrysum* and *Rhodanthe* show daily opening and closing movements and were found by experiment to respond to different levels of humidity in the same way as described for *Acroclinium*. *Ammobium* and *Xeranthemum* show little daily movement in the field, unless rain raises the humidity level, when closure follows, frequently at night. The bracts in all cases are green at the base and show the maximum curvature at the junction between this and the scarious areas. The closing movements of *Ammobium* and *Xeranthemum* are slow and imperfect.

Flower cycle of *Ptiloria tenuifolia*

Flower cycle of *Acroclinium roseum*

VI

ESCHSCHOLTZIA CALIFORNICA, MENTZELIA LINDLEYI, AND SIMILAR FLOWERS

ESCHSCHOLTZIA CALIFORNICA

FIELD BEHAVIOR

Eschscholtzia californica is a common garden plant coming into the blooming period at Colorado Springs in July and continuing until frost. The buds are erect and are enclosed by a green calyx cup which is torn free from the base at the first opening of the flower and forced off by the expanding base of the corolla cone. The petals open at 7 to 9 A.M. and close during the afternoon, repeating these movements on 4 to 6 successive days. The anthers open at the first or second expansion of the petals, and the stigma is exposed on the succeeding day. In closing, the petals roll spirally, as in the bud, forming a compact cone which encloses the stamens and pistil. The older flowers open slightly before the younger, the first opening of a flower usually being completed an hour after the older neighbors have reached complete expansion. As the end of the active life of the flower is approached, closure becomes irregular and incomplete. Frequently the petals of old flowers do not close into a compact cone but roll individually, forming four conical rolls with the stamens and pistil exposed between. The opening movement requires about one hour, bringing the petals to an angle of 110°. The petals of old flowers frequently roll out along the longitudinal axis and drop singly, those remaining continuing their movements until detached. Following the fall of petals the ovary remains in the upright position and elongates during the development of the ovules (Plate 13).

FIELD EXPERIMENTS

Closed flowers of *Eschscholtzia* heated to 25° in a bell jar in the field opened if this treatment was before the normal time of opening. The application of the same temperature in the afternoon, following closure, resulted in an opening movement, but this took place at a lower rate and did not proceed to complete expansion. The flowers closed when cooled to 18.5° from 11 A.M. to 12 M. Covering with shade tents produced no noticeable result unless the shelters were made of light-proof cloth, when early closure followed, probably as a result of the increase in temperature within such a tent. Flowers heated to 35° in a bell jar in the field closed slightly before adjacent

113

normal ones. Cut flowers exposed in the bed with a supply of water opened and closed normally for 2 or more days. When stored at 10°, darkness, and 100 per cent humidity for 24 hours, they opened readily at any time of day when the temperature was raised to 20°, 25°, or 30°.

In the region of the most active curvature, *Eschscholtzia* flowers showed a considerable mass of parenchymatous tissue, many of the cells containing yellow chromatophores. The intercellular spaces were small compared to those found in the corolla of the Compositae. The inner epidermis was more heavily cuticularized than the outer, the cuticle forming protuberances above each cell. The thin places facilitated curvature inward, and the entire inner epidermis exerted considerable tension in that direction, as may be seen from the immediate rolling of this layer when torn free from the underlying tissue.

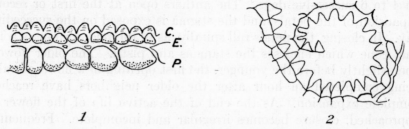

FIG. 21.—Cross sections of the corolla of *Eschscholtzia californica* through the basal region

1 inner epidermis (E) with cuticle (C) and underlying parenchyma cells (P) x 450, and 2 inner epidermis rolled when torn free from the underlying tissue.

The structure of the inner epidermis, and the action when free from the other tissues, are shown in Figure 21. No functional stomata were observed on either surface in the active region of curvature. The corolla, being so well protected, showed a very low rate of transpiration, but this rate could not be correlated with the position of the flower.

LABORATORY EXPERIMENTS

Ecostat experiment on the flowers of *Eschscholtzia* were carried out according to the methods already described. Since a sufficient supply of flowers was not available at the laboratory, most material used was stored in the thermostat at 10°, darkness, and 100 per cent humidity, during the transportation from the field and until the beginning of the experiments. The number of hours of such storage preceding the experiment is recorded in each case.

Table 19 gives the average behavior of 20 freshly cut flowers, and flowers on potted plants, at various constant conditions of 15°. 20°, and 30° temperature, darkness, and 50 per cent humidity.

Flower cycle of *Eschscholtzia californica*

TABLE 19

ESCHSCHOLTZIA CALIFORNICA

Behavior (per cent open) of cut and
potted flowers subjected to constant conditions of darkness and 50% humidity, and
to various constant temperatures.

Flowers	Freshly Cut			Potted
Temp. °C.	15	20	30	30
Time				
6:30 a.m.	1	28	11	5
9:30	0	0	0	60
11:30	4	25	80	90
1:30 p.m.	4	60	89	90
4:30	4	77	85	72
5:30	0	35	48	30
6:30	0	5	8	0

The response curves are given in Figure 22. These show that
under constant conditions cut flowers of *Eschscholtzia* opened during
the morning, and closed in the late afternoon, the delay in the rhythm
being due to cutting during the beginning of expansion. Flowers
growing on potted plants showed a similar periodic rhythm, but
lacked the shock effects of cutting and hence reached maximum expansion sooner. The periodic opening tendency, if delayed by shock,

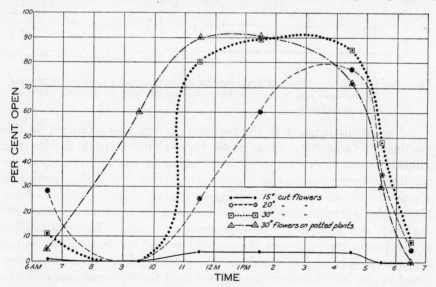

FIG. 22.—Percentage opening of flowers of *Eschscholtzia californica* under constant
conditions of darkness and 50 per cent humidity, and 15°, 20°, and 30° C.

is effective at the given temperatures in producing an opening movement later in the day.

Table 20 gives the average behavior of 2 to 5 flowers at various conditions of temperature and periods of storage. The number of hours storage at constant conditions of 10°, darkness, and 100 per cent humidity is given at the head of each column and shows the time between cutting in the field and installation in the experimental chamber under the temperature conditions given, darkness, and 40 per cent humidity.

Typical response curves are shown in Figure 23.

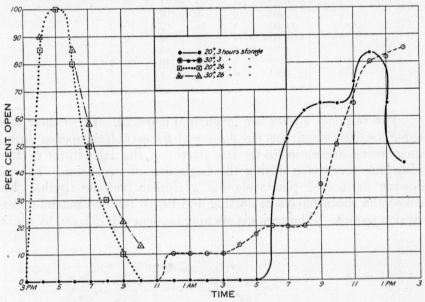

Fig. 23.—Behavior of flowers of *Eschscholtzia californica* under constant conditions of darkness and 40 per cent humidity and 20° and 30° C., after different storage periods.

A great disturbance in the periodic rhythm was produced by this treatment (Table 20). Thus, as shown in Column No. 1, the opening reaction immediately followed installation in the 30° chamber, the maximum being reached at 2 P.M.; in Column No. 2 this maximum appeared only on the day following treatment at 30°; and in Column No. 3 the reaction immediately followed installation in the 30° chamber, the maximum being reached at 5 P.M. The explanation of this lies in the nature of the periodicity and its dependence on the preparation period for opening. Considering first the material exposed in the 30° chamber, the flowers used for the reactions given in Column No. 1 were cut at 1 P.M. shortly before the normal closing period and stored under conditions that prevented all opening move-

Column No.	1	2	3	4	5	6	7	8	9	10	11	12	13	14	15	16	17	18	19	20	21	22	23	24	25	26
Temp. °C.	30						25					20							15			30 to 20			20 to 30	
Hours Storage	11	3	26	6	9	15	16	18	18	9	11	3	26	6	9	15	16	18	26	9	16	6	6	6	3	3
Time																										
12 m.	0	0	0	0	0	0	0	0	0	0	0	0	0	0	0	0	0	0	0	0	0	0	0	0	0	0
1 p.m.	61	0	90	0	12	15	37	20	13	9	22	0	85	0	8	18	10	5	0	0	5	0	0	0	0	0
2	82	0	100	0	30	25	70	60	70	23	63	0	100	0	18	25	17	50	0	0	5	0	0	0	0	0
3	80	0	85	0	48	35	95	85	70	35	75	0	80	0	28	40	23	78	0	0	5	0	0	0	0	0
4	75	0	58	0	70	75	90	90	88	55	75	0	50	0	50	80	85	85	0	0	8	0	0	0	0	0
5	63	0	30	0	75	90	92	95	95	65	60	0	30	0	30	90	90	85	0	0	5	0	0	0	0	0
6	50	0	22	0	83	90	94	93	95	66	41	0	10	0	18	90	90	87	0	0	0	0	0	0	0	0
7	30	0	13	0	83	90	95	95	18	66	23	0	0	0	15	80	90	55	0	0	0	0	0	0	5*	0
8	15	0		0	50	80	73	70	12	50	15	0		8	11	50	63	40	0	0	0	0	0	5	5	0
9	13	0		15	15	64	50		8	30	15	0		8	8	25	42		0	0	0	0	0	15	8	0
10	10	0		15	11	38	18		6	10	15	0		8	8	18	13		0	0	0	10*	0	35	12	0
11	5	10		15	6		10		4	10	5	0		8	8	10	3		0	0	0	10	5	45	15	0
12 mt.	0	10		25	5		9		0	5	0	30		8	8		3		0	0	0	5	5	45	15	0
1 a.m.		13		25	5		8			5		52		15	8		3		0	0	0	5	5	45	20	0
2		17		25	5		5			5		62		18	8		0		0	0	0	10	5	43	27	0*
3		20		20	5		5			5		65		18	8		0		0	0	0	10	5	45	33	0
4		20		20	5		5			5		65		30	5		0		0	0	0	10	5	44	33	10
5		35		30	5		0			5		73		38	3		0			0	0	10	23*	45	33	28
6		50		50	5		0			5		83		20						0	0	5	20	30	33	45
7		65		50						5		65		10						0	0	5	20	26*	30	48
8		80		45						0		43		5						0	0	0	20	20	40	52
9		82		40						0				5						0	0	0	20	0	53	60
10		85		30										5						0	0	0	18	0	65	60
11				28										3						0	0	0	18	0	70	65
12 m.				25										3							0	0	18	0		70
1 p.m.				20										3								0	35	0		
2				15										0								0	35	0		
3				10										0									35	0		
4				5																			35	0		
5				0																						
6																										
7																										
8																										
9																										
10																										
11																										
12 mt.																										

ments for 11 hours. An opening reaction immediately followed the change to 30° and continued to 82 per cent completion. Column No. 4 shows the behavior of flowers cut at 1 P.M. and given less than one-half (6 hours) of the preparation period at 10° before changing to 30°. No reaction followed the change for 7 hours and it was delayed and reduced in amplitude, the maximum of 50 per cent having been reached at 1 P.M. The flowers for which results are shown in Column No. 7 were cut at 2 P.M. After 16 hours storage these opened immediately to full expansion when changed to 30°. This shows that preparation for opening progressed better under the conditions of 10°, darkness, and 100 per cent humidity than at 30°, darkness, and 40 per cent humidity.

The flowers used in the experiments the data for which are given in Columns No. 2, 3, 5, 6, and 8, were cut at 12 noon during the open period. Column No. 2 shows that after 3 hours storage and closure the flowers showed no opening for 8 hours after the change to 30°, and that the expansion which then followed was delayed and of decreased amplitude. There was a period of 14 hours from the beginning of opening to the maximum of 85 per cent. The flowers used for results given in Column No. 5 received 19 hours storage. When changed to 30° the opening response was immediate and progressed to a higher degree of expansion. Flowers the data for which are given in Columns No. 6 and 8 received 15 and 18 hours storage and agreed in displaying immediate response of large amplitude when changed to 30°.

The results of experiments at 20° show a perodic relation similar to that at 30°, indicating that preparation for opening in *Eschscholtzia* does not progress appreciably better at 20° than at 30°. Since other experiments showed that preparation went on normally at 15°, there is perhaps a threshold value lying between 15° and 20°. The change from the thermostat to 20° constituted a less intense stimulus than the change to 30°. The periodicity of *Eschscholtzia* flowers is apparent in a comparison of the time of response following the changes. Thus in Columns No. 2 and 12 it is evident that when preparation was incomplete and the resulting movements slow, the delay following the change to the experimental chambers was greater at 20° than at 30°. It is probable that this delay is not a latent period during which the effect of the stimulus is becoming apparent, but represents the time required for the sum of the periodic opening tendency and constant temperature to become effective. Thus at 30° (Column No. 2), opening began at 12 MT., but at 20° not until 6 A.M. (Column No. 12). As the preparation became more complete this temperature difference decreased until it vanished when the preparation period had been 11 hours or more. The response to a sudden change in temperature between 30° and 20° showed a periodicity. Thus in Columns No. 22, 23, and 24, changes from 30° to 20° at 6 A.M. checked the extent of the reaction; at 12 noon this check was temporary and was later followed by further expansion, and at 3 P.M. no noticeable change in the closing reaction resulted. Changes in the opposite direction at 10 P.M. and 3 A.M. showed no difference in response.

Periodicity in the flowers of *Eschscholtzia* is determined by the daily cycle of habitat factors, as Stoppel has already reported for other species. The period during which the flower is closed constitutes a preparation for opening, and this preparation does not proceed normally at temperatures of 20°, 25°, or 30°, and largely disappears after 24 hours of constant conditions. The conditions obtaining during the preparation period are as important as those during the periods of movement in determining the floral reaction, the rate, time, and extent of opening depending on the preparation as well as on the factors obtaining at the time of movement.

EFFECTS OF TEMPERATURE

Table 19 and Figure 22 show results and curves for a daily period computed from 20 flowers of *Eschscholtzia* under each temperature condition given. All flowers closed after cutting, immediately re-opened in a curve proportional to the temperature, the maxima being 4, 77, and 89 for the rising temperatures, and the rates of opening to a maximum after recovery from cutting, 4, 11, and 22. The degree-hours required for reaching a maximum opening at 30° was 210 for the cut, and 150 for the uncut, and at 20°, 200. That is, the temperature-time requirement for opening was similar at 30° and 20° for cut flowers, but these values were considerably increased by the shock of cutting over those obtained from potted flowers under similar conditions. Cutting during the closed period did not produce this shock effect, and if time for recovery were allowed before the opening reaction it did not affect the behavior curve.

From the preceding discussion of the effects of periodicity, it is clear that a comparison of the effects of temperature on the flowers of *Eschscholtzia* can be made only between flowers having the same treatment before the experiment. The results of 30° and 20° constant temperature after 3 hours storage may be seen in Columns No. 2 and 12, Table 20. Here the unfavorable conditions of the preparation period delayed the response and limited the reaction. Change to 30° resulted in an opening movement beginning 9 hours after the change to this temperature and continuing to a maximum of 85 per cent at an opening rate of 3.7, while at 20° movement began after 14 hours, continuing to a maximum of 83 per cent at an opening rate of 4. That is, temperature effects appeared under these conditions in delayed initiation of response rather than in rate or extent of opening. Where the preparation was more nearly complete, as after 6 hours storage (Columns No. 4 and 14), the rate and extent of opening varied directly with the temperature, the values being 2.8 and 50 at 30° and 2.2 and 38 at 20°. With a preparation approaching normal, 9 hours storage (Columns No. 5, 10, 15, and 20), the rate and magnitude of opening varied directly with the temperature, the maxima and rates being 83 and 14, 65 and 11, 50 and 12.5, and 0 and 0, for 30°, 25°, 20°, and 15°, respectively.

With 15, 16, and 18 hours of storage (Columns No. 6, 7, 8, 9, 16, 17, 18, 21) the differences between 30° and 20° were small, approximately full opening occurring under both conditions. At 15° a slight periodic opening occurred. After 26 hours storage (Columns No. 3 and 13, Figure 23), an opening reaction to full expansion followed immediately at 30° and 20°, the rate being 50 in both cases. At constant temperature levels the flowers of *Eschscholtzia* responded according to the temperature conditions obtaining at the time of opening, and also the conditions and length of the preparation period. Freshly cut flowers and those subjected to short periods of storage at 10°, darkness, and 100 per cent humidity, expanded according to the daily rhythm in the field at a rate and to a degree varying directly with the temperature level between 15° and 30°. Storage in the thermostat under the conditions just given favored the opening reaction so that the difference in the effect of a change to either 30° or 20° disappeared after 26 hours storage. Preparation for opening was not complete by 6 P.M. in the 10° chamber, and the opening which followed at 30° or 20° was delayed and limited in extent. No opening reaction occurred at 15°, except in one case where a slight periodic movement took place. Columns No. 22 to 26 show the results of sudden changes between 30° and 20°. After 6 hours storage the opening reaction was delayed and limited under constant conditions of 30° and 20°. Columns No. 22, 23, and 24 show that changes made from 30° to 20° at 6 A.M., 12 M., and 3 P.M. limited the extent of the reaction, but did not appreciably hasten closure except at 3 P.M. when the periodic action agreed in direction with the movement. When the reverse change was made at 10 P.M. and 3 A.M., an opening reaction followed after a latent period of one hour, progressing slowly to a greater degree of expansion than that in the flowers with similar storage at 30° constant. It seems probable that this temperature change constituted a stimulus to opening, the result of which was an increase in the initial opening to a greater degree of expansion than would occur under similar but constant conditions.

This is in contrast to the effects of constant temperatures, which do not seem to constitute a stimulus but to control the expression in movement of internal stimuli. Experiments the details of which are not given here, showed that changes in temperature between 30° and 15° made during the course of movement increased the rate of opening when the temperature rise was made during the opening movement, but did not check closing when a similar change occurred during the process.

EFFECTS OF LIGHT

The average reactions of flowers of *Eschscholtzia* kept at 25°, 50 per cent humidity, and .275 and 40 foot-candles light intensity are given in Table 21, and two curves are shown in Figure 24. All flowers were cut in the field immediately before installation in the

TABLE 21

Eschscholtzia Californica

Behavior (per cent open) of flowers subjected to constant conditions of 25°, 50% humidity, and light intensities of .275 and 40 foot-candles.

Light Conditions Time	.275 Foot-candles				40 Foot-candles			
9:30 p.m.	2				2			
12 mt.	2	2			2	0		
3:30 a.m.	2	2	5		2	0	5	
5	2	2	5		2	8	6	
6	2	2	8	4	2	17	14	2
7	8	5	14	10	2	19	37	27
8	29	15	28	36	2	8	52	54
9	77	36	65	63	2	13	65	75
10	83	62	92	72	4	8	65	85
11	88	73	100	100	4	8	56	81
12 m.	88	90	100	100	13	4	37	77
1 p.m.	85	62	81	63	13	2	2	25
3	45	31	38	35	10	0	0	13
4	38	18	22	25	8	0	0	13
5	22	14	9	10	6	0	0	12
6	19	12	9	9	6	2	0	13
12 mt.	19	2	9	9	6	2	0	13

experimental chambers, which were maintained at 25° and 50 per cent humidity.

The various series placed in the ecostat at 9:30 P.M., 12 MT., 3:30 A.M., and 6 A.M. showed the relations to length of preparation periods at the low night temperatures of the field, and periodic movements similar to those already discussed. There was also a distinct inhibiting effect of 40 foot-candles light intensity as compared to that

of .275 foot-candles. This inhibition of the opening reaction may
be seen to have affected the amplitude of expansion by the maxima
which, for the series in the order of starting times, are 88, 90, 100,
and 100, for .275 foot-candles, and 13, 19, 65, and 85 for 40 foot-
candles. This shows that 40 foot-candles light intensity reduced the
maxima expansion in all cases, but particularly in the earlier series
where it was applied during a portion of the preparation period.

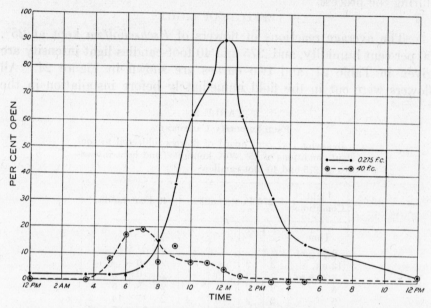

Fig. 24.—Percentage opening of flowers of *Eschscholtzia californica* under constant
conditions of 25° C. and 50 per cent humidity, and different light intensities.

Frequently it was observed, as shown in Figure 24, that the
maximum opening was attained earlier at 40 than at .275 foot-candles,
this condition being indicated in all cases in Table 21 except in
the 9:30 P.M. series. The rates of opening also show the inhibition
due to light. For the series in the order given the opening rates are
6.4, 7.3, 12.7, and 19.2, at .275 foot-candles, and 0.8, 2.7, 9.2, and
20.8, at 40 foot-candles. This shows that the extent of opening was
more strongly reduced by the intense light than the time for reaching
their expansion was hastened.

Intense light, like high temperatures, is unfavorable for the preparation for opening of flowers of *Eschscholtzia,* reducing the extent
and rate of the ensuing reaction in proportion to the amount of the
preparation time so lighted; but during opening the movement is
hastened to the maximum by the more intense radiation.

EFFECTS OF HUMIDITY

Studies on the effects of humidity on the opening and closing of *Eschscholtzia* gave variable results. No stimulation effects were found, but at 90 per cent saturation the open period of flowers was longer than at 25 per cent.

TISSUE STUDIES

When the epidermis was stripped from the petals of *Eschscholtzia*, in the basal region where the most active curvature occurred, there was usually an immediate bending toward the uninjured side, followed by the withering of the structure. The epidermal layers were evidently exerting a tension on the structure, and in the adjustment of the opposing tensions of the inner and outer layers movement occurred. When the outer epidermis was removed and the petal placed in water, or in sucrose solutions of .15, .20, or .25 molar, a closing movement resulted, but with decreasing speed and amplitude as the concentration was increased. In .30 molar sucrose solution little or no movement occurred, and in .40 molar a slight opening resulted. Plasmolytic studies were carried out on the epidermis of flowers growing in the field, the hourly determinations being made on the opposing epidermis stripped from a single petal.

Figure 25 gives the average differences in the concentration of the plasmolyzing solutions and the percentage opening of the flowers, positive numbers indicating higher concentration in the outer epidermis, and negative numbers the reverse relation.

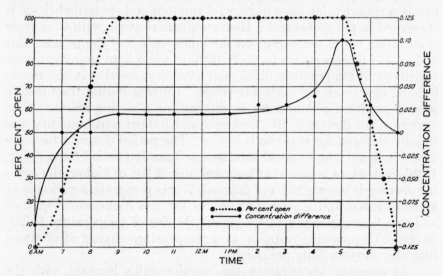

FIG. 25.—Percentage opening of flowers of *Eschscholtzia californica*, and the difference in osmotic concentrations between the cells of the inner and outer epidermis in the region of active petal curvature.

It will be seen that preceding the opening of the flowers the concentration of the inner epidermal cells was greater than that of the outer, that during opening this difference was equalized, and that the concentration of the outer epidermis gradually rose during the day above that of the inner, the greatest rise immediately preceding floral closure. During the closing reaction the concentrations of the epidermis approached, and reached equality as the process was completed. Flowers kept in the ecostat showed a similar relation of concentration and movement.

It is evident that floral movements in *Eschscholtzia* are preceded and accompanied by changes in the relative concentration of the cells of the opposite epidermis, such that an opening and closing movement of the petals followed high concentrations in the inner and outer epidermal cells. These concentrations fell to equality during the open or closed period, decreasing when the flower was open, and rising when it was closed.

SUMMARY

The flowers of *Eschscholtzia* are hemeranthous, opening and closing daily, but the calyx dropping at the first opening. Field experiments showed that heating to 25° or 35° causes early opening of closed flowers and premature closing of open ones. Shading produced no apparent effects other than thermal. Cut flowers behaved normally in the field, unless stored at 10° for 24 hours or more, after which they opened following exposure to field conditions at any time during the daylight period. In the region of most active curvature in the petals, a considerable mass of parenchymatous and epidermal tissue is concerned in the movement. Heavy cuticularization, with thin areas to facilitate curvature, occurs on the inner surface of the petals. Cut and potted flowers showed a daily rhythm when kept under constant conditions of temperature, light, and humidity, opening in the morning and closing in the early afternoon. Cutting during the opening process produces a temporary shock, causing a closing reaction. The storage of cut flowers at 10°, darkness, and 100 per cent humidity materially changes the periodic behavior. The period during which the flower is closed may be considered as a preparation period for opening. If this is short, or is passed at temperatures of 20° or higher, the ensuing opening is incomplete and delayed; if this preparation period is 11 hours or more, and is passed at 10° to 15° and darkness, immediate and complete expansion follows a sudden rise of temperature to 20° or 30°. The opening response to a temperature change of constant intensity shows a daily periodicity.

At constant temperature the reaction rates increase with the length of the storage period at 10°. Thus, if periodic differences are eliminated by considering only flowers cut at the same time (12 M) and changed to 30°, the reaction rates of 3.5, 14, 15, 19, and 50, are found at the storage periods of 3, 9, 15, 18, and 26 hours. When all the series are considered together, the effects of a complicated double variable of periodicity and length of storage are revealed. With freshly cut flowers the rates of opening are proportional to the constant temperature, little or no reaction occurring at 15°. On the other hand, low temperatures favor preparation for opening. When cut flowers are stored at 10° for a period approximating the length of the normal storage, the rate and extent of opening is proportional to the temperature; when the storage period is of greater length than normal, this temperature difference disappears. Sudden increases in temperature stimulate the opening reaction.

A light intensity of 40 foot-candles inhibits the opening movement of the flowers, particularly when it is applied during a portion of the preparation period, this effect appearing as a reduction in both the extent and rate of opening. This intensity hastened the time at which the maximum openings were attained. High humidities increased the length of the open period of the flowers, and decreased slightly the extent of expansion. Plasmolysis of the epidermal cells in the region of maximum curvature shows that the movement of the corolla occurs in the direction of decreasing concentration of the cell sap.

SIMILAR FLOWERS

The flowers of *Papaver dubium* in the field behave like those of *Eschscholtzia*, the calyx cap being forced off at the first opening and the corolla carrying out two successive cycles before falling. *Papaver hybridum*, *P. argemone*, and *Glaucium corniculatum* open with a similar action, but are ephemeral and collapse after a single day. Experimental studies were not made on these species, which seemed similar in behavior to *Eschscholtzia*.

MENTZELIA LINDLEYI
FIELD BEHAVIOR

Buds of *Mentzelia lindleyi* are produced on short erect peduncles. The calyx lobes are slowly pushed apart by the growing corolla, which elongates to slightly less than twice the length of the sepals. As the bud matures, the sepals become slightly yellowish. With the elongation and opening of the corolla the sepals are forced open and remain thus, curling partly along the midrib, and finally withering before the fruit matures.

The first opening of the bud occurs during the forenoon, but at varying times with different buds which are in an apparently similar habitat and exposure. The openings after the first are more uniform as to time. During July the opening process begins about 7:30 A.M. and requires one and one-half hours for completion. The petals curve back largely from the basal region and flatten laterally. The stamens bend out, the movement progressing centripetally during the 2 to 4 days of activity. Opening occurs on 2 to 4 successive days, the flowers closing about 7 P.M. The petals then wither in a loosely closed condition and drop away (Plate 14).

Field readings show such great variability that one can safely conclude merely that the temperature and light intensity are rising and the humidity falling when opening takes place, and that a reverse change is in progress at the closing time. Shading or watering immediateley before and during the opening process exerts an evident influence. Flowers open at the normal time if cut and kept supplied with water in the habitat; old flowers close slowly, but show little change in time or rate of opening.

LABORATORY EXPERIMENTS

Studies carried out on *Mentzelia lindleyi* in the ecostat were limited in number. The averages from the results of two experiments carried out in darkness and under the conditions listed in the different columns are given in Table 22.

TABLE 22
MENTZELIA LINDLEYI
Behavior (per cent open) of flowers
at various constant temperatures and
humidities.

Temp. °C.	15	25	20	20
Humidity %	40	40	25	75
Time				
6 a.m.	0	0		
7	0	0	0	0
8	0	21	15	13
9	2	43	27	30
10	5	80	60	58
11	18	100	94	83
12 m	20	100	100	88
1 p.m.	20	100	100	90
2	20	97	89	90
3	20	94	84	90
4	20	90	78	90
5	12	83	67	75
6	7	70	50	61
7	0	50	30	41
8	0	10	12	11

Results in columns 2 and 3 reveal a periodic daily rhythm of movement under various constant conditions of temperature, dark-

Flower cycle of *Mentzelia lindleyi*

ness, and 40 per cent humidity. The percentage maximum expansion was 20 at 15°, and 100 at 25°, with opening rates of 5 and 25 for these two temperatures. Columns 4 and 5 indicate that at 75 per cent humidity the degree of expansion was slightly reduced and the duration of the maximum increased, in comparison with the 25 per cent chamber. Thus at 20° and 25 per cent humidity the percentage maximum expansion was 100, lasting 2 hours, and at 20° and 75 per cent humidity the maximum was 90 with a duration of 4 hours. The relation of the flowers to light was uncertain. Two experiments showed no constant relation between movement and light intensities of 40 and .275 foot-candles, since opening and closing occurred in light and darkness at equal rates.

SUMMARY

The flowers of *Mentzelia lindleyi* are hemeranthous, expanding on several successive days. They have a daily rhythm, but the rate and amplitude of expansion vary with the temperature. The flowers exhibit no definite relation to the light intensities used, but show slightly greater expansion in low humidities and a longer open period in high.

ROSA ACICULARIS

Rosa acicularis occurs abundantly on the moist north slopes in the vicinity of the Alpine Laboratory at 8300 feet elevation, where the flowers open in the early morning and close in the late afternoon. The tips of the sepals and the corolla carry out the movements, opening in the early morning and closing in the late afternoon on 2 to 4 successive days. As the flowers age, closure may be imperfect or entirely prevented.

LABORATORY EXPERIMENTS

The behavior of the flowers of *Rosa acicularis* at various constant conditions of temperature, darkness, and 35 per cent humidity is given in Table 23. Since these experiments were carried out at this low humidity (35 per cent), this factor was limiting at the higher temperatures and resulted in the wilting of the flowers, rendering them unsuitable for further readings. All material was cut in the field immediately before the beginning of the experiment in which it was used.

Flowers cut at midnight and kept at 30°, 20°, and 10° showed a periodic opening in the early morning, the experimental conditions of the chambers in no case producing an opening reaction in the afternoon. The importance of the preparation period and its relation to temperature was similar to that already discussed for other species. Thus at 30°, full expansion occurred in every case, but the opening rates from the first movement to maximum opening varied from 20 to 33 and 32, the low value having been obtained from the series with a portion of the preparation period at 30°. Similarly at 20°, the 7 P.M. series, with the preparation period at this temperature, showed an opening rate of 7.3, while for the series left in the field during this period the rates were 33 and 30. At 10°,

TABLE 23

Rosa Acicularis

Behavior (per cent open) of flowers subjected to various constant conditions of temperature, darkness, and 35% humidity, after different preparation periods.

w. flower wilted and readings abandoned.

Temp. °C.	10	10	10	20	20	20	30	30	30
Time									
7 p.m.	0			0			0		
8	0			0			0		
9	0			0			0		
10	0			0			0		
11	0			0			28		
12 mt.	0	0		0			55	0	
1 a.m.	0	0		8	40		85	50	
2	0	0		15	90		90	80	
3	0	0		25	100		100	100	
4	0	0		25	100		100	100	
5	0	0		25	100		100	100	
6	0	10	0	30	100	0	w	100	0
7	0	15	0	40	w	50	w		60
8	0	18	0	40		75			80
9	35	18	15	40		90			95
10	45	18	55	40		90			95
11	45	20	12	55		90			95
12 m.	45	24	15	68		90			95
1 p.m.	45	27	15	95		90			95
2	40	27	15	95		90			95
3	35	12	15	95		90			95
4	21	6	12	95		90			95
5	12	0	5	95		90			95
6	5	0	0	95		90			95
7	0	0	0	95		90			95

preparation for opening continued normally as was shown by the opening rates, the 7 P.M. series giving a rate of 23, as against 3.4 and 4 in the later series where a portion of the period was spent in the field at temperatures averaging above 10°.

A comparison of the series started at the same time—that is, with a similar preparation period—shows a temperature effect on the opening process. Thus at 30°, 20°, and 10° the maxima were

100, 95, and 45 in the 7 P.M. series; 100, 100, and 27 in the 12 MT. series; and 95, 90, and 15 in the 6 A.M. series. The rates of opening were complicated by the temperature effects on the preparation period, and by the fact that low temperatures delayed the opening as well as reduced the degree. When preparation was completed in the field (12 midnight and 6 A.M. series), there was little difference at 30° and 20°, the values being about 30 for all series; but at 10° a considerable reduction was shown. When the preparation period took place in the chambers, 10° gave the highest values, as discussed in the preceding paragraph, and 20° the lowest. Apparently 20° and 30° were equally unfavorable for preparation, but the higher temperature furnished the stronger opening stimulus and thus more nearly compensated for this.

TISSUE STUDIES

In the region of most active movement both in sepals and petals of *Rosa acicularis* there is a considerable mass of parenchyma which doubtless acts with the epidermis in producing the curvature of the organ. Plasmolyzing solutions of sucrose showed that in the open flower the inner and outer epidermal layers were of equal concentration, but below that found in the unopened bud, the respective values being .6 M and .9 M. Immediately before opening at 5 A.M. the values of the bud had fallen to .7 M for the outer epidermis and .75 M for the inner. A preliminary study of the epidermis of the calyx showed that during the open period the concentrations were .6 M for the outer surface and .7 M for the inner.

As in the species previously discussed, the flowers of *Rosa acicularis* exhibit a differential concentration of the cell sap of the epidermis on the two surfaces, with movement in the direction of decreasing concentration.

TRIBULUS TERRESTRIS

Tribulus terrestris is an interesting hemeranthous form, because the flower movements are similar to those occurring in the old flowers of some other species. The buds, enclosed in the pubescent green calyx, are produced on short peduncles beneath the prostrate stems. As the time of opening is approached, the bud is carried into an upright position and the grooved stigma extruded. The flowers open about 9 A.M., the petals apparently forcing back the calyx and exposing the anthers clustered below the stigma. In closing during the early afternoon, the petals roll individually along the midrib and close together in this form, the sepals making but little movement. At the second opening the stamens spread and the anthers open and the petals are then usually shed, the carpotropic movements placing the developing ovary beneath the stem again.

Since *Tribulus* occurs in dry exposed situations, and the usual closure is like that of old flowers of forms like *Eschscholtzia* in which the water content has reached a low level, it seems that the rapid desiccation of the flowers of *Tribulus* may account for their similar behavior. Flowers were enclosed in vials with the walls moistened to test this assumption. Although the temperature in the vials was several degrees higher than that in the surrounding air, the desiccation rate was greatly reduced by the increased humidity and the prevention of air currents, and flowers thus enclosed in the field did not show the longitudinal rolling of the petals characteristic of the neighboring unprotected ones. Usually the flowers in the field did not show rolling when rains were frequent or the soil moist. Buds opened at the usual time in the ecostat chambers under constant conditions of 20° and 30°, 25 per cent humidity, and darkness or 40 foot-candles light intensity. Rolling did not occur, the flowers either remaining open until withering, or closing without rolling. The individual rolling of the petals seems to be the result of a severe desiccation of the tissues, which frequently occurs in *Tribulus* because of the nature of the habitat, but happens only in old flowers of plants growing under more favorable conditions. Plate 15 shows the typical stages in the floral life history of *Tribulus*.

Flower cycle of *Tribulus terrestris*

VII

THE GENTIANS, AND OTHER EPHEMERAL HEMERANTHOUS FLOWERS

GENTIANS

FIELD BEHAVIOR

Gentiana calycosa, G. amarella, and *G. frigida,* the three species of gentians studied, occur commonly in the mountains at Colorado Springs, *G. amarella* at altitudes of 7000-10,000 feet, *G. calycosa* at 9000, and *G. frigida* at 11,000. The flowering season is from August until frost, beginning earliest for *G. amarella* and latest for *G. frigida.* These hemeranthous flowers open from 7 to 8 A.M. The tips of the corolla lobes expand and are gradually reflexed to an angle of 30° to 50°, the filaments spreading during the process. Closure begins at sundown and requires an hour for completion. The calyx shows no activity, but the movements of the corolla are repeated on 4 to 6 successive days. Plates 16 and 17 show the opening of the flowers of *G. amarella,* and *G. frigida.*

Temperature readings made in the field in close proximity to the flowers showed that opening began in the morning at 20°, 18°, and 8°, for the flowers of *G. amarella, G. calycosa,* and *G. frigida,* while the average temperature for closure of the species in the order given was 16°, 12°, and 5.5°. Observations showed that at times the temperature at opening was no higher than that at closing. Autumn storms occasionally produced a sharp fall in temperature which resulted in the closing of the flowers if it occurred at noon or after and was not too severe. After storms which reduced the temperature to 5° or lower, the flowers remained open throughout the night but resumed normal movement the following day. Cut flowers exposed in the field behaved similarly to uncut ones throughout a period of several days.

Uncut flowers in the field when enclosed in a bell jar heated to 20° opened somewhat earlier than adjacent ones in the atmosphere at 12° to 14°. Early closing could also be induced by cooling the bell jar 2° to 4° below the temperature of the surrounding air in the late afternoon; but flowers could not be kept closed during the forenoon by covering with a bell jar cooled to 12° to 14°, or reopened by heating to 20° immediately after closure.

131

GENTIANA AMARELLA

LABORATORY EXPERIMENTS

Experiments were made to test the behavior of the flowers of *Gentiana amarella* under constant conditions of 10°, 20°, and 30°, at 50 per cent relative humidity, and darkness. All material was freshly cut in the field and placed immediately in the experimental chambers. Three series were studied. In the first, the flowers were placed in the ecostat chambers at 6 A.M. when opening was under way, some flowers being still closed and others open; the second was started at noon when all flowers were fully expanded; and the third at 3 P.M. when the usual open period was drawing to a close.

At a constant temperature of 10°, flowers in the process of opening at 6 A.M. remained in the condition in which they were installed in the chambers, and on the second day carried out their usual daily opening and closing reaction. Fully open flowers placed in the 10° chamber at 12 noon and at 3 P.M. closed at once, the process requiring about one hour. At 20°, flowers cut at 6 A.M. in the open condition carried out the usual daily cycle of movement, closing at 6 P.M.; but if the opening movement had only begun, the flowers expanded to about 50 per cent in three hours and closed at the usual time of those in the field. The open flowers placed in the 20° chamber at noon remained open until 8 P.M. and then closed incompletely, while those brought from the field at 3 P.M. remained open until 8 to 9 P.M. and then closed partly. Flowers in process of opening at 6 A.M. when placed in the 30° chamber, completed the process and then closed at 6 to 8 P.M. When cut at noon or at 3 P.M. all flowers in the 30° chamber remained open until 6 to 8 P.M. when closing occurred. Flowers kept in the 10° and 20° chambers carried out their usual cycle of movement on the second day, but at 30° all remained closed.

Changes in temperature between 10°, 20°, and 30° were made at different times during the day, but since the two higher temperatures gave results which differed chiefly in degree, only those resulting from changes between 10° and 30° will be detailed here. To test the opening response at various times before the usual daily closing period, flowers cut at 6 A.M. were changed from 10° to 30° at 2, 4, and 6 P.M.; and flowers cut at noon and at 3 P.M. were subjected to a similar change in temperature. At 2 P.M. the flowers of the 6 A.M. series, which had been partly open in the field and then held in the 10° chamber, opened at once; those in the noon series, which had been closed by exposure to 10°, opened 10 per cent; and those in the 3 P.M. series failed to react. When the temperature change was made at 4 P.M. no response occurred. Changes from 30° to 10°

7 A.M.

7.45 A.M.

8 A.M.

Flower cycle of *Gentiana amarella*

were made at 10 A.M. and 3 P.M. The flowers in the 6 A.M. series, which had been opened in the 30° chamber, when placed in the 10° chamber at 10 A.M. remained open until 2 P.M., after which closure occurred. When a similar transfer was made at 3 P.M., closure began at once but required 3 hours for completion. Flowers of the noon series, when transferred at 3 P.M., exhibited movements entirely similar to those shown by the 6 A.M. series, closing in 3 hours. The flowers in all series closed within one hour when transferred from 30° to 10° at 6 P.M.

It is evident from these results that the flowers of *Gentiana amarella* show a periodic closing at 6 to 8 P.M. under constant conditions of 20° and 30°, and that this periodicity is checked at 10° constant temperature. This daily periodic movement occurs on the second day under constant conditions, but only at the lower temperature, not being evident at 30°. Flowers in the process of opening, when changed from 10° to 30° responded by immediate opening; but closed flowers subjected to the same change in temperature opened only in the forenoon when the direction of the periodic tendency and that of the stimulus agreed. Similarly, a sudden change of temperature from 30° to 10° caused the closing of open flowers only in the afternoon when the periodic and stimulus directions were the same. The time from the transfer to the 10° chamber to the completion of the closing reaction decreased as the time of normal closing approached. Irrespective of the periodic behavior, a direct relation between the maximum degree of expansion and the temperature level was apparent, the flowers remaining closed at 10° and opening to greatest extent at 30°. A similar relation between the temperature and the closing rate was evidenced.

Subjecting flowers of this species to constant temperatures and to alternating temperatures brings out the fact that a temperature alternation, at least, is necessary to effect complete movement reactions when that temperature is approximately the mean of those in the field. Thus at 20° constant there is positive evidence of periodic movement, but an incomplete reaction. How far the alternation of other factors may contribute to the completeness of reaction was not determined, but it can safely be concluded from studies on other species that temperature alternation is most important.

Apparently 10° C. is below the optimum for movement of flowers of this species. However, it is significant that the normal daily cycle of movement occurs during the second 24-hour period at this temperature. As in the "hardening process" in plants, it may be concluded that some protoplasmic adjustment occurs after a long period of exposure. It is important to note in this case that periodicity is not destroyed.

Since in this species the greatest movement does not take place at the insertion of the corolla but well up this structure at the base of the lobes, epidermis from this region was examined. The cells here are cuticularized and rounded up into short papillae. Plasmolytic studies showed that the concentration of the epidermal cells both on the inner and outer surfaces increased toward the tips of the petals. For this reason it was difficult to make comparable determinations on opposing cells, and the results showed considerable variability. Although a distinct daily cycle was evident, the concentrations being low in the morning and increasing during the afternoon, the relation to floral movement was not established.

GENTIANA CALYCOSA
LABORATORY EXPERIMENTS

Fifty flowers of *Gentiana calycosa* were used in three series of experiments to determine the relation of floral movements to temperature, and the periodicity relations at various temperature levels from 10° to 30°. The average percentage opening is shown in Figure 26. At 20° the flowers opened immediately when placed in the ecostat chambers at 8 P.M., and showed no further movement until 10 o'clock the following morning when a slow closing occurred. In contrast to this behavior the flowers kept at 10° and 30° showed nothing but the initial movements. At 10° there was an immediate completion of the closing process already under way in the field when the flowers were cut, and no further opening during the course of the experiment. At 30° the flowers opened rapidly, the rate being 85, and remained open throughout the period of the experiment. Thirty degrees seemed close to the maximum for *G. calycosa*, for in two cases the flowers when only partly expanded closed quickly and permanently.

Two series of flowers were alternately shifted at hourly intervals between the 10° and 30° chambers, so that one set was being subjected to 10° while the reciprocal set was held at 30°. The resulting movements agreed throughout the experiment, all flowers responding by an opening movement when placed in the 30° chamber, and by a closing reaction in the 10°. A portion of a single curve is given in Figure 26, the reciprocals and second series agreeing closely with the behavior here shown.

The opening and closing responses were of equal intensity from the beginning of the experiment until 8 A.M., after which the degree of opening gradually decreased. The experiment was prolonged to 36 hours, 10 hours beyond the extent shown in the graph, and showed this characteristic to the end, the percentage maximum expansion decreasing to 50. Since this decrease was not altered during the two morning periods over which this experiment extended, it is evident that the effect was not due to periodicity but rather to a failure of

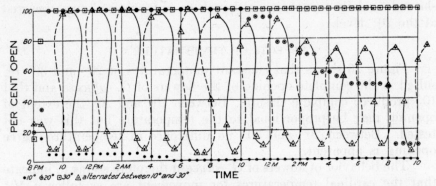

Fig. 26.—Percentage opening of flowers of *Gentiana calycosa* under constant conditions of darkness and 50 per cent humidity, at different temperature levels, and when alternated between 10° and 30° C.

the flowers to reach maximum expansion in the time interval given. When removed from the experimental chambers and placed in the field the flowers opened fully. The decreasing amplitude of movement in the experimental chambers evidently resulted from the incompleteness of the reaction in the time allowed between the temperature changes. Under these conditions the reaction rate in response to temperature changes between 10° and 30° showed no daily periodicity but a gradual decline with the duration of the experiment. It can easily be assumed that this behavior is of the nature of a fatigue reaction. If this be true it further emphasizes the assumption that the time interval between movements was too short.

Opening rates computed from results of observations on all plants changed between 10° and 30°, and averaged in 4-hour periods to reduce variation in the different series, show the following average hourly opening rates for the periods between the times given:

Temp. °C.	10–30	10–20
Time Periods		
8 p.m. to 12:30 a.m.	87	76
12:30 a.m. to 4:30 a.m.	89	79
4:30 a.m. to 8:30 a.m.	89	78
8:30 a.m. to 12:30 p.m.	85	76
12:30 p.m. to 4:30 p.m.	73	66
4:30 p.m. to 8:30 p.m.	73	58
8:30 p.m. to 12:30 a.m,	55	62
12:30 a.m. to 4:30 a.m.	50	52

This shows no evidence of daily periodicity, the rates decreasing during the course of the experiment irrespective of the time of day. A series begun at 8 A.M. gave results similar to these, as did also a midnight series in which potted plants were used. The flowers showed no daily periodicity, although an autonomic closure occurred at the 20° level.

EFFECTS OF TEMPERATURE

Figure 26 shows that constant temperatures of 20° and 30° resulted in the complete opening of the flowers of *G. calycosa* and that 10° produced complete closure. Between 10° and 20° the extent of opening may be proportional to the temperature but this was not tested. Between 20° and 30° no difference in temperature-degree opening is apparent.

The behavior of flowers of *G. calycosa* therefore seems to indicate that the cardinal temperatures for movement are as follows: 10° lies below the minimum for stimulus to open, the minimum lies between 10° and 20°, the optimum between 20° and 30°, and the maximum above 30°. This is also borne out in the experiments described below.

Sudden changes in temperature between 10° and 30° resulted in immediate opening, the degree varying with the length of the period in the experimental chambers. Similar reactions followed changes between 10° and 20°, but the extent of the opening and the rate of reaction was slightly less than that following a change to the higher temperature. The average percentage maximum opening of flowers changed from 10° to 20° was 90, and from 10° to 30° was 98, considering only the first six hours of the experiment before any progressive decrease in the opening was apparent. The opening rates just given show that values following changes from 10° to 20° were but slightly lower than those following changes from 10° to 30°.

A temperature change from 10° to either 20° or 30° initiated a floral opening to nearly the same degree, as measured by the rate of reaction. The reaction rates in both series follow much the same curve of decrease in the progress of the experiment. All flowers which were transferred between 20° and 30° agreed in showing little or no closure, the expansion curve being practically a straight line at 100 per cent open. For the first ten hours of the experiment there was usually a slight closure following a change from 30° to 20°, but after this initial period all flowers remained fully expanded. If the rates of opening are considered for the initial period of the experiments, they are 78 and 8 for the series changed from 10° to 20° and from 20° to 30°, respectively. As measured by the rate of opening, a temperature change of 10 degrees is nearly ten times more effective from 10° to 20° than from 20° to 30°. This coefficient is high and indicates that the resultant of forces at play in floral movement is more rapidly displaced than in most plant reactions.

TISSUE STUDIES

Plasmolytic studies on *Gentiana calycosa* were made on the cells of the epidermis in the region of maximum curvature at the base of the corolla lobes. The pigmented and unpigmented cells in this area showed considerable difference in osmotic pressure. Examinations at 4 A.M., 1 P.M., and 8 P.M. gave the following average results, based on study of the pigmented cells, and expressed as percentage molarity concentration of sucrose solution.

Epidermis	Outer	Inner
Time		
4 a.m.	0.65	0.60
1 p.m.	0.60	0.50
8 p.m.	0.60	0.60

These results are not conclusive, but seem to show that the variation in concentration in the epidermal cells is but slight, and that these variations do not correlate with the floral movement except in so far as the fall in concentration during the open and opening periods may indicate a hydration phenomenon. *G. calycosa* is one of the few species studied by the authors wherein there is only the slightest evidence of periodicity. It varies markedly from *G. amarella* in this respect, but is similar to *G. frigida*.

GENTIANA FRIGIDA

In the field the flowers of *G. frigida* are frequently subjected to low temperature and to sudden and extreme changes. The flowers open and close frequently during their active life, but often close imperfectly, and occasionally remain open throughout the night. Plate 17.

LABORATORY EXPERIMENTS

Material for the laboratory studies was obtained from the alpine meadows at an elevation of 12,500 feet and brought in large pieces of soil to the laboratory, with as little disturbance as possible to the plants. They were placed in an open north exposure where the temperature was 4°, and the flowers were removed at the beginning of the experiments.

Series were started under constant temperature conditions at midnight, 6 A.M., and 6 P.M. Closure could be maintained by temperatures of 5° or less, the flowers opening at any temperature from 10° to 30°. At 10°, closed flowers opened in 5 hours, giving an opening rate of 20; at 20° the opening required 3 hours, with an opening rate of 33; and at 30° opening took place in one to one and one-half hours, the average opening rate being 75. No periodicity was shown under constant conditions.

Opening could be induced at any time of the day by the transference of the closed flowers from 5° to 10°, 15°, 20°, 25° or 30°. Sudden changes in temperautre between 10°, 20°, and 30° were made in two series of experiments, one started at 12 midnight, the other at 12 noon. The flowers opened and closed in varying degrees to temperature changes between 10° and either 20° or 30°. Since these changes were made at short intervals, complete opening or closing did not result, but in every case the movement initiated by the ensuing change began with little or no delay. That is, if during the course of an opening or closing movement the temperature stimulus was changed, movement in the opposite direction occurred immediately. A typical curve is shown in Figure 27.

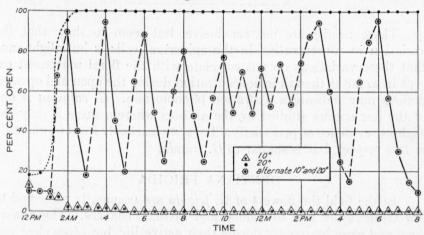

Fig. 27.—Behavior of flowers of *Gentiana frigida* at 10° and 20° C., and when alternated between these temperatures.

Changes between the 10° and 20° chambers were at first made at intervals of two hours, and from 10 A.M. to 2 P.M. at half-hour periods. It is evident that neither the time of day nor the stage of movement altered the response to the temperature change, the flowers showing a closing reaction when placed in the 10° chamber and an opening response when transferred to the 20° chamber at any time during the day or at any point in the course of the opposite move-

Flower cycle of *Gentiana frigida*

ment. The flowers of *G. frigida,* like those of *G. calycosa,* do not show
a daily periodicity of movement.

Under constant conditions of temperature, humidity, and light,
the flowers of *G. frigida* opened and remained open, but the rate of
opening varied with the temperature. The degree of expansion did
not correspond with the temperature level at which the flowers were
maintained. When temperatures were suddenly changed, opening
was initiated by a rise from 10°, and closing by a fall to this temperature. The magnitude of the response did not differ with the intensity
of the stimulus, but was the same after a change from 10° to 20°, and
from 10° to 30°. The flowers remained expanded when changed at
hourly intervals between 20° and 30°, but when similarly rapid
changes were made from 10° to 20° and 30° the flowers responded with
decreasing amplitude. The opening rates in series changed at hourly
intervals between 10° and 20° decreased from 49 at the beginning
of the series to 13 after 24 hours. Comparable values for the 10°
to 30° series were 60 and 16, and for the 20° to 30° series 10 and 0.
In consequence, it is evident that this does not show a fatigue curve
but an interruption in the reaction under way at the time of the temperature stimulus which reversed the reaction before its completion.
Since this reversal occurred earlier in the course of the reaction proportional to the duration of the experiment, as is shown by the decreasing opening rate, there must have been a summation of the
factors inhibiting floral movement and these factors must have persisted from one reaction to the next. It may be that in the flowers of
G. frigida there is an irritability phenomenon for which the sudden
temperature change is the stimulus. Thus a rise from 5° to 10°
opened the flower, but a fall from 20° to 10° closed it.

The results of plasmolytic studies seem to agree with this conclusion, for the cells of the outer epidermis were uniformly more concentrated than those of the inner. The concentration throughout the
tissues of the petals, as well as the difference between the inner and
outer layers, was greatest in the closed bud and least in the open
flower.

LINUM RUBRUM
FIELD BEHAVIOR

The mature buds of *Linum rubrum* open from 6 to 7 A.M. by
unrolling the corolla cone which at this time projects 5 mm. or more
beyond the tips of the calyx lobes. During the opening process, which
requires about 2 hours, the calyx is forced apart and the petals spread,
exposing the anthers and stigma. If at this time the calyx is artificially opened, the petals expand at once, their opening largely
dependent on the force of the expanding corolla. The corolla

closes from 12 M. to 4 P.M., depending on weather conditions, and commonly in July and August withers during the night and following morning, dropping by 10 A.M. without reopening. Thus the flowers at this season are ephemeral. During May and June, when the weather conditions are less severely desiccating, the flowers open on 2, 3, or even 4 successive days. The flowers are thus hemeranthous during the cooler seasons, but ephemeral hemeranthous during the warmer months. Cut flowers exposed in the field behaved like those which were undisturbed. Plate 18 shows the floral life history.

LABORATORY EXPERIMENTS

Table 24 gives a summary of the behavior of the flowers under constant conditions of 50 per cent relative humidity, darkness, and temperature levels of 10°, 20°, and 30°.

TABLE 24

LINUM RUBRUM

Behavior of flowers subjected to constant conditions of 50% relative humidity, darkness, and temperature levels of 10°, 20°, and 30°C.

Time	Temp. °C.	Percentage Max. Expansion	Time of Max. Expansion	Hours Latent	Opening Rate
7 p.m.	10	20	10 a.m.	8	3
12 mt.	10	33	9	3	5
6 a.m.	10	40	10	2	20
7 p.m.	20	63	10	6	7
12 mt.	20	60	10	3	9
6 a.m.	20	90	8	0	45
7 p.m.	30	65	8	10	22
12 mt.	30	85	8	0	15
6 a.m.	30	95	8	0	48

It is evident that the flowers of *Linum rubrum* showed a well marked daily periodicity. Thus, at all temperatures tested, the latent period decreased with the approach of the morning opening period. The combined averages for the three experimental temperatures for the different periods give a latent period, expressed in hours, of 8, 2, and 1, for 7 P.M., 12 midnight, and 6 A.M. The nearer the time of starting the series to that of the normal daily opening period, the more quickly the reaction followed. That is, the preparation for opening is favored by field conditions and connection with the plant, as compared to any of the constant temperatures tried.

Table 24 shows the responses of the flowers of *Linum rubrum* to the different temperature levels. Thus in the 7 P.M series the percentage maximum expansions are 20, 63, and 65, and the opening rates 3, 7, and 22, for 10°, 20°, and 30° respectively. In the same order of temperatures the midnight series shows the maximum expansions 33, 60, and 85, and the opening rates 5, 9, and 15. For the 6 A.M. series the comparable values are 40, 90, and 95, and 20, 45, and 48. It is evident that, in the temperature range tested, the amplitude and consequently the rate of opening varied directly with the temperature, but that the time of opening was largely controlled by internal factors. In experiments not detailed here it was found that a sudden temperature change from 20° to either 15° or 30° at 6 A.M. constituted a stimulus for opening, the change resulting in the expansion of the flower to a degree dependent on the temperature level at which it had been maintained. The closing rates, though variable, did not show a positive correlation with temperatures between 10° and 30°.

The percentage water content of the open flowers was 81.5 in the green weight, and 79.1 in the partly collapsed flowers. Plasmolytic studies were complicated by the fact that the pigmented cells differ in concentration from those which are pigment free. In general the highest concentrations occurred in the unopened bud where values averaged .45 and .30 molar for the plasmolyzing sucrose solutions in the inner and outer epidermis respectively. In the fully open flower these values had fallen to about one-half, although they still maintained the same relation to each other. In the collapsing flower the osmotic values had further decreased, with the inner epidermis still showing a slightly higher osmotic pressure than the outer. It appears that if the osmotic pressure of the epidermal cells is effective in floral movement in *Linum rubrum*, it could function only in the opening, and is not directly concerned in the changes that follow.

SIMILAR FLOWERS

In the field the flowers of *Calochortus gunnisoni* and *Agrostemma githago* open on three or more successive days before becoming inactive. Studies on these flowers showed periodicity and temperature relations similar to those of *Linum*. In both flowers a change in temperature from 10° to either 20° or 30° produced an opening reaction only if made when periodicity favored the opening movements.

The flowers of *Godetia grandiflora* show a daily opening and closing movement, the calyx remaining inactive in the open condition. During the early summer season the flowers open at 8:30 A.M. and close at 6 P.M., the movements requiring one and one-half hours and being repeated on 4 to 6 successive days. Late in the summer this period of floral activity is shortened so that at times the flowers remain open but a single day before collapse. As in the case of *Linum rubrum*, the flowers are ephemeral or hemeranthous, depending on the desiccating conditions of the habitat in which they occur. By the plasmolytic method it was determined that the epidermal cells showing the highest concentration occur in the bud in which there is also the greatest difference between the inner and outer surfaces of the petals, the values obtained being respectively .55 and .35 molar. As the flower opened, the concentration of the outer epidermis rose to the level of that of the inner.

PORTULACA GRANDIFLORA

The flowers of *Portulaca grandiflora*, like those just discussed, may be either hemeranthous or ephemeral, opening on two or more successive days or collapsing after a single expansion period. The flowers, which open by 10 A.M. and close at 5 P.M., are enclosed by two calyx lobes which are inactive and forced apart by the expanding corolla.

Under constant conditions of darkness, 50 per cent relative humidity, and temperature levels of 10°, 15°, 20°, and 30°, the flowers showed a periodic opening, except at 10° where they remained inactive. Thus, when placed in the ecostat at 12 midnight, the flowers remained closed at 10°, opened at 7 A.M. at 20°, and at 6 A.M. at 30°. When cut at 5:30 A.M. no movement took place at 10°, but opening resulted from 6 to 7 A.M. at both 15° and 30°. The percentage degree of opening varied with the temperature, being 0, 60, and 75, for 10°, 20°, and 30° respectively. Sudden increases in temperature resulted in opening movements only when the daily periodicity agreed in direction. When flowers in the process of opening were changed from 20° to 10° at 8 A.M. the movement was stopped but no closure could be observed. Similarly a change from 10° to either 20° or 30° at midnight did not result in an opening movement until 6 to 7 A.M., when opening occurred in the checks which were held at a constant temperature like that to which the change was made.

OTHER EPHEMERAL HEMERANTHOUS FLOWERS

Hemeranthous flowers, which in the habitat conditions of Colorado are commonly ephemeral, may last two or three days if the weather conditions are very favorable for reducing the desiccation rate. The flowers discussed under this heading are ephemeral throughout the flowering season except during cool foggy weather, differing in degree from such flowers as those of *Linum rubrum* or *Portulaca*.

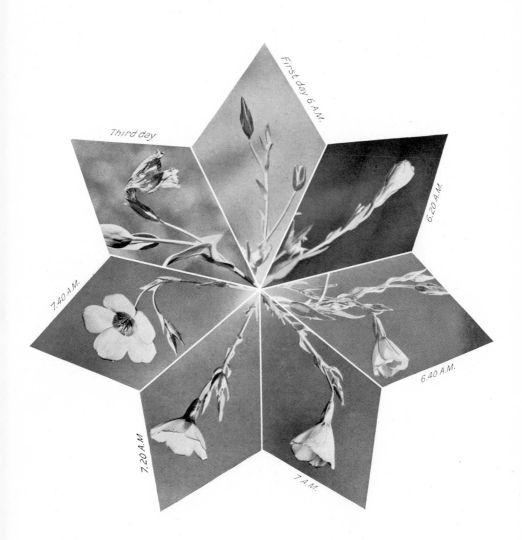

Flower cycle of *Linum rubrum grandiflorum*

In field behavior these flowers agree in opening in the morning and collapsing during the day. The flowers of *Malva rotundifolia* and *Abutilon theophrasti* open from 7 to 10 A.M. and close from 5 to 6 P.M., often remaining closed throughout cold days. *Anagallis grandiflora, A. arvensis* and *A. coerulea* open at 8 A.M., the first two closing from 2 to 3 P.M., and the third an hour later. *Gilia densiflora*, which opens as early as 7 A.M. and does not close until 4 to 5 P.M., may be taken as an example of the group. Following the elongation of the corolla cone the petals curve out and unroll, the calyx taking no essential part in the movement. Closure may or may not be accompanied by partial collapse.

In laboratory experiments under constant conditions the flowers showed a periodic opening in the morning at 15°, 20°, and 30°, but remained closed at 10°. With a relative humidity of 25 per cent the maximum opening occurred at 20°, partial collapse intervening before the opening process was complete at 30°. Closure occurred in the late afternoon, unless the collapse of the petals had resulted previously. Plasmolytic studies of the epidermal cells showed a low osmotic concentration which was uniformly higher on the inside of the petals during the opening and open condition.

Erodium cicutarium is a somewhat more ephemeral type of flower than those just discussed. The stigma is frequently exerted a day before the opening, which occurs from 4 to 5 A.M. and requires about thirty minutes. The calyx is reflexed and the petals spread, finally assuming an angle of more than 180 degrees. By 1 P.M. both calyx and corolla close, and the petals are shed during that day or the following.

HIBISCUS TRIONUM

FIELD BEHAVIOR

The flowers of *Hibiscus trionum* show a remarkable ephemerality, opening before 6 A.M. and closing from 10 A.M. to 12 M. The floral behavior is shown in Plate 19. During the night and very early morning the elongation of the corolla cone forces apart the corolla lobes and projects beyond their tips. The unrolling of the petals begins by 5 A.M. and the flower is completely open within 1 hour, the petals elongating considerably during the process. Flowers remain open 3 to 5 hours, depending on weather conditions, and close by the rolling together of the somewhat flaccid petals. The drying remains of the corolla are held for several days by the closed calyx before dropping free. After the floral opening the calyx remains closed until forced apart by the enlarging fruit. When the desiccating conditions are severe the flowers remain open but a short time before closing permanently, while on cool days the open period frequently extends well into the afternoon. Temperature readings in the field showed that flowers open with a rise in temperature from 12° to 13.5°, and close at 25°.

LABORATORY EXPERIMENTS

Flowers of *Hibiscus trionum* for experiment in the ecostat chambers were selected during the night preceding the opening, as only after the corolla had begun to elongate was it possible to choose with surety buds which would open normally the next morning. The buds were cut in the field and immediately placed in the experimental chambers, or were stored under constant conditions and later transferred to the chambers. Buds cut during the night and left supplied with water in the field opened at the approximate time of those remaining attached to the plant, only if the cutting were done at 12 midnight or after. Buds cut before this time behaved erratically and frequently remained closed, indicating in this case a relation to the mother plant.

PERIODICITY

The necessity for attachment of the buds of *Hibiscus trionum* to the plant until 5 to 6 hours before the opening period, made observations under constant conditions unsatisfactory. Flowers were cut and placed in the experimental chambers at 10 P.M., 12 midnight, and 2, 4, and 6 A.M. Temperatures of 10°, 15°, 20°, 25°, and 30° were employed, with a relative humidity of 50 per cent, and light values from darkness to 40 foot-candles. In every case it was obvious that the temperature change to the experimental chambers acted as a stimulus for opening. If an opening reaction did not result on installation of the flower in the chambers, it did not follow later under constant conditions. The maximum expansion was attained in the five series from 10 P.M. to 6 A.M., 1.5, 2, 2.6, 2.1, and 1.7 hours after the flowers were placed in the ecostat chambers. Buds placed in the chambers at 10 P.M. remained permanently closed, except in the 30° chamber where a slight opening movement occurred followed at once by closure. Changes between 10°—the approximate temperature in the field during the night period—and temperatures up to 30° did not result in opening if made before 10 P.M.

Figure 28 shows the opening rates of the flowers following their removal from the field and immediate installation in the experimental chambers. The curves show the daily periodic relations. At 10 P.M., opening followed only when the buds were placed in the 30° chamber; at midnight, opening followed at the three higher temperatures, but showed low values which increased in the 2 A.M. series, and reached maximum values at 4 and 6 A.M. It is evident

Flower cycle of *Hibiscus trionum*

that at temperatures above 10°, at which periodicity is suppressed, these flowers open in a periodic cycle beginning at 10 P.M. and proceeding to a maximum at 4 to 6 A.M., when opening usually occurs in the field. This periodicity may be expressed as the rate of open-

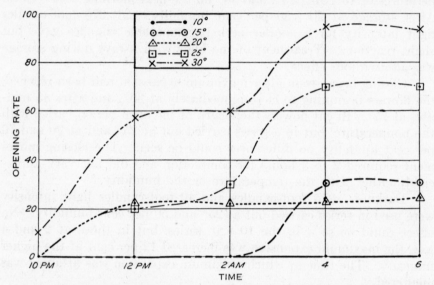

Fig. 28.—Opening rates of flowers of *Hibiscus trionum* when transferred from the field to different temperature levels at various times of day.

ing or by the maximum openings attained. Thus at 30° for the series 10 P.M., 12 MT., 2 A.M., 4 A.M., and 6 A.M. respectively, the flowers opened to the angles of 20, 42, 92, 93, and 70, respectively. Although the highest values appear earlier than when the opening rates are considered, a periodic fluctuation is evident.

EFFECTS OF TEMPERATURE, HUMIDITY, AND LIGHT

The flowers of *Hibiscus trionum* show a distinct temperature relation. Figure 28 shows that the opening rates were highest at 30°, and zero at 10°, with the intermediate curves falling between these values. At midnight and at 2 A.M., when the periodic opening tendency is great enough so that a reaction followed a change to 20°, 25°, and 30°, the values at 20° and 25° differed but little. During the period of maximum periodicity, values obtained at 15° and 20° were similar, but at 25° and 30° gave far higher results. Apparently there is a threshold of stimulation which is passed by a change to 30°, but not by that to 25° until it is lowered by the maximum periodicity.

Experiments to determine the effects of different storage conditions were not satisfactory because of the uncertainty of obtaining mature buds at definite periods before their opening time. Cut buds and those on potted plants did not open when placed at 0°, 100 per cent humidity, and darkness at 5 P.M. and changed to temperatures of 15°, 20°, 25°, and 30° on the next morning at 6 o'clock. After storage at 20°, 50 per cent humidity, and .275 foot-candles light intensity for a similar period, comparable changes gave but slight reactions. Treatment of the buds with x-rays during storage was also without effect.

Closing began soon after maximum expansion had been reached, the flowers beginning to close immediately at 30°, and after 45 minutes at 15°. In cut flowers the length of the open period varied with the temperature, but in a series carried out at 25° and at 20 and 70 per cent humidity no differences could be seen. The closing movement required 2 to 3 hours for completion and did not vary appreciably either with the temperature or the humidity.

Darkness, .275 foot-candles and 40 foot-candles light intensity were used in series carried out at 25° and 50 per cent humidity. No effect could be seen in the 10 P.M. series, but in those at 2 and 4 A.M. the maximum expansion was increased 12 per cent at the higher intensity. The time at which maximum expansion was attained was unaltered.

TISSUE STUDIES

Plasmolytic studies on *Hibiscus trionum* were made with material freshly cut in the field, and with that kept under experimental conditions. Figure 29 shows the curve of osmotic concentration for the outer and inner epidermis of flowers fresh from the field at the times indicated. This shows that during the night, before the opening movements appeared, the concentration of the inner epidermal cells increased over that of the outer; this difference disappeared during the opening process, and approached equality with that of the outer during the entire open period. During closing, the concentration of the inner layer of cells increased again, and then fell rapidly as the petals collapsed. This final decline may not represent an increase in the osmotic concentration of the solutes in the cell sap, but a loss of the semi-permeability of the cell membrane accompanying senescence.

In flowers stored at 30° the osmotic relations accompanying the induced opening became involved. A change to 30° in the early morning, resulting in an opening movement of the flower, lowered the concentration of the inner epidermis to the level of that of the outer, but there was no recovery of concentration, as occurred in the field, when the flowers closed. At 20° this recovery period appeared. At 10° the concentrations remained in the condition of those found in

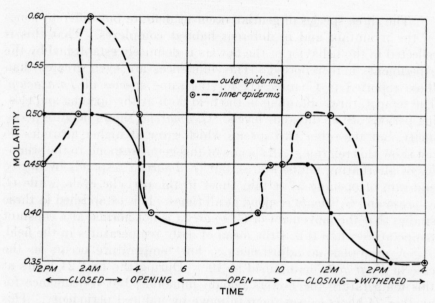

FIG. 29.—Osmotic concentrations of the epidermal cells of *Hibiscus trionum* expressed as the molarity of hypertonic sucrose solutions.

the bud. Opening in the flowers of *Hibiscus trionum* is probaly accompanied by the greater hydration of the inner tissue than of the outer. The consequent enlargement of the cells probably accounts for the curvature on which the opening of the corolla depends.

SUMMARY

Most flowers considered in this chapter may be hemeranthous or ephemeral hemeranthous, depending on the rapidity of desiccation during their open period. The gentians are largely hemeranthous, *Linum rubrum* and the portulacas may be either, *Erodium* is only exceptionally hemeranthous, and *Hibiscus trionum* never reopens on the second day and usually remains expanded but a few hours.

Periodicity is shown by all the flowers except *Gentiana frigida* and *G. calycosa,* in which it was not detected by the methods used in this study. In most cases the daily periodic movements can be suppressed at 10°, and the duration of the open period reduced at 30°. Humidity and light have little or no effect.

The flowers show a direct relation between the rate of opening and the degree of expansion and temperature. These gentians respond readily throughout the day to sudden temperature changes, the degree of the response decreasing with the length of the experiment. The other flowers discussed respond only when the direction of the stimulus and that of the periodic movement agree.

The three species of gentian occur at definite but different zones on the mountain and in different habitat complexes. That this is reflected in the behavior of the flowers is definitely established by the experiments here reported. The differences are even greater than those reported in Chapter III for the same species of *Taraxacum*. The temperatures obtaining in the field both at the opening and closing periods are at different levels. *G. amarella* shows definite periodicity, but the other two species which grow at higher altitudes do not show this relation. All species of this genus respond to the stimulus of alternating temperatures, but *G. amarella* responds by degree and rate of opening at certain times in the periodic cycle, while *G. calycosa* and *G. frigida* respond at all times. It is established in these studies that the movement of *G. amarella* is not normal at a constant temperature when this is the mean of daily temperatures in the field.

A protoplasmic adjustment to low temperature occurs in the case of *G. frigida* maintained at 10°. During the first 24 hours at this temperature the flowers remain immobile, but continuance for another 24 hours causes them to move by induced periodicity. This is thought to be a reaction similar in nature to the well known "hardening process" of plants.

The opening of flowers in response to stimuli is probably the expression of a summation of internal factors. This is clearly the case in *G. frigida* where the expression is very pronounced, and it is not unlikely, though less clearly demonstrated, that certain reactions obtained in other species may depend on this.

The osmotic concentration of the epidermal cells shows no relation to floral movement in the gentians, but in the other flowers discussed it indicates that opening is accompanied by a decreasing concentration in the surface from which the movement occurs. This is believed to indicate an increasing water content, and hence turgidity in the cells. Closure is closely accompanied by the senescence and collapse of the cells, and the plasmolytic method reveals a falling concentration in both surfaces of the petals.

VIII

MENTZELIA NUDA AND MENTZELIA MULTIFLORA

MENTZELIA NUDA

FIELD BEHAVIOR

Mentzelia nuda is common along roadsides and in waste places in the vicinity of Colorado Springs. Although this plant is typically of the plains, it occurs along the mountain roads at elevations up to 10,000 feet where it mingles with *M. multiflora* and produces hybrid forms. The large creamy white flowers open about 5:30 P.M. and close two hours or more later. Opening and closing is repeated on 7 to 8 successive days before the petals become inactive with age, wither, and drop to the ground. The calyx lobes, which at first are imbricated to enclose the bud, are forced apart by the growing cone of the corolla. Twenty-four hours before the first expansion of the flower the tips of the sepals are reflexed. With the spreading of the petals on the following afternoon additional curvature occurs, after which the calyx shows no further movement, remaining recurved and dry on the mature fruit. Plate 20 shows the typical movements of the first and second days and the beginning of collapse on the fifth day.

The opening of the corolla requires one hour or more, and the closing the same length of time. Although the time of day at which opening occurs does not vary greatly, the time of closing is subject to wide variations. At times many flowers will be found open throughout the night. Factor readings are not always consistent on these occasions and it seems probable that the behavior of the flowers at these times is conditioned by the predetermining environmental factors. During the solar eclipse of September 1923 most flowers opened in the field by 3:50 P.M., although on the preceding and succeeding days the completion of the process was nearly an hour later.

FIELD EXPERIMENTS

Watering the soil about the plant of *Mentzelia nuda,* or removing the calyx lobes, did not alter the floral behavior. Cut flowers kept in the vicinity of those undisturbed on the plant behaved normally during the first 48 hours at least. A quick drop in temperature to 16° was observed to check the opening process at its beginning and to keep the flowers closed throughout a 24-hour period.

To test the effects of various factors on the movement of these flowers, two branches of a single plant were covered by large bell jars, and the remainder of the plant was left exposed to the air undisturbed. The bell jars were heated or cooled by circulating hot or cold water through coils enclosed with the experimental plant. A thermometer and dew-point apparatus were also placed within the bell jars for purposes previously described. Temperatures of 30° and 25° were maintained with a humidity which varied around 80 per cent. The time of opening was not very different from that of the free flowers. Under these conditions a reduction in the light, produced either by shading or by the declining of the sun, was followed by the opening of the flowers. A single typical experiment may be given as an example. Five flowers at 30° in bell jars began to open at 5 P.M. simultaneously with those on the same plant which were in the open; a third portion of the plant, which was enclosed under a bell jar treated in the same manner as the first but shaded at 4 P.M., showed open flowers in one-half hour after shading.

LABORATORY EXPERIMENTS

Table 25 gives the average percentage opening of flowers of *Mentzelia nuda* under conditions of constant temperatures of 15°, 20°, 25°, and 30°. The values given are the averages from 3 to 5 individual flowers, and agree in all essentials with the behavior of flowers of this species in other experiments. The flowers were kept at 50 per cent humidity and darkness throughout the experiment, a light of 0.275 foot-candles being turned on momentarily to make angular reading possible. All the flowers used in this experiment were cut at 5:30 P.M., brought into the laboratory and stored at 12°, 100 per cent humidity, and darkness, until the beginning of the experiment. Flowers which had been open in the field for one daily period only were selected.

PERIODICITY

It will be seen that there was a characteristic and well marked periodic cycle of movement, the flowers under the constant conditions of the three higher temperatures opening in the late afternoon and closing by midnight in a manner similar to the field behavior already described. In the 7 A.M. series, the values for which are graphed in Fig. 30, periodic opening appeared at all temperatures tried, although the movement was limited by the temperature and hence slight at 15°. After 24 hours in the experimental chambers a second periodic opening and closing occurred, and while this movement was changed in extent it was not significantly altered in time. In the second opening the degree of movement was reduced at the two

Flower cycle of *Mentzelia nuda*

TABLE 25

MENTZELIA NUDA

Behavior (per cent open) under various constant conditions of temperature, 50% relative humidity, and darkness.

Temp. °C.	15	15	15	20	20	20	25	25	25	30	30	30
Time												
7 a.m.	0			0			0			0		
10	0	5		0	10		0	3		0	5	
11	0	5		3	10		0	3		0	5	
2 p.m.	0	5	10	3	10	7	0	3	7	0	5	0
3	3	5	10	7	10	8	0	3	7	0	5	0
4	3	5	10	7	10	8	5	3	7	10	5	0
5	3	5	10	18	10	8	75	5	8	100	5	2
6	3	5	10	25	10	8	75	7	53	100	17	25
7	3	5	10	25	10	8	70	7	50	90	20	25
8	5	5	10	20	10	8	60	10	40	85	20	25
9	5	5	10	10	10	8	52	22	30	80	22	25
12 mt	5	5	10	8	10	18	10	7	27	0	22	27
3 a.m.	5	0	0	7	3	10	11	7	20	0	15	17
7	3	0	0	5	3	10	8	5	20	0	7	17
10	3	0	0	5	3	10	8	5	20	0	7	17
1 p.m.	3	0	0	5	3	7	9	5	18	5	5	17
3	3	0	0	5	3	7	9	5	18	5	5	17
4	5	0	0	8	3	22	26	8	23	60	7	17
6:30	33	10	30	23	55	38	51	25	32	85	52	17
9	18	5	13	12	35	37	36	22	32	40	50	17
10:30	23	5	8	12	30	28	27	15	25	35	30	15
12 mt.	0	0	0	0	6	5	3	3	7	5	4	8

higher temperatures but increased at 15°. During the low temperatures of storage and of the 15° chamber the amplitude of the periodic movement of the flower increased, the low temperatures being favorable for the preparation period.

The flowers placed in the experimental chambers at 10 A.M. and 2 P.M., after receiving 3 and 7 hours more storage during the daylight hours, showed great variability but in general opened near the usual time for opening in the field. Storage at 12° during the night increased the amplitude of movement, but when the flowers were subjected to these conditions during the day the extent of the periodic opening was reduced and the time of expansion delayed or made more variable. This was shown in a more striking manner by other flowers placed in the experimental chambers at 3 P.M. or later. Little or no movement occurred at any temperature from 15° to 30°. The amplitude of the periodic opening was inversely proportional to the storage period at 12°, 100 per cent humidity, and darkness, during the daylight period. When storage was only during the night, as in the 7 A.M. series, the periodic opening at 30° was complete expansion.

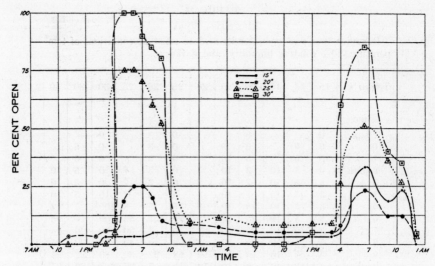

FIG. 30.—Behavior of flowers of *Mentzelia nuda* at various temperature levels, 50 per cent relative humidity, and darkness.

Under constant illumination the flowers of *Mentzelia nuda* showed showed the same periodicity as appeared in darkness (Table 26), opening and closing at approximately the time at which these movements occurred in the field. When suddenly changed between light intensity of .275 and 40 foot-candles the daily periodic movements were still evident, as is shown in Table 27. Changes in illumination influenced the movements only at the time of the daily periodic reaction. With changes from low to high illumination at 8 and 11 A.M. and 4 and 6 P.M., all flowers began expanding from 5 to 7 P.M. It is evident that any effects of illumination on the movements of the flower merely modified the periodic behavior.

EFFECTS OF TEMPERATURE

Table 25 and Figure 30 show that after storage the flowers of *Mentzelia nuda* opened to a maximum expansion proportional to temperatures from 15° to 30°, when the 7 A.M. series is considered. The flowers kept in storage until later in the day displayed various modifications of this relation, since storage at 12°, 100 per cent humidity, and darkness during the daylight period reduced periodic movements. Thus when placed in the experimental chambers at 10 A.M. no movements occurred during the first 24 hours at 15° and 20°, while those exhibited under the two higher temperatures were equal. When the flowers were removed from storage and installed in the chambers at 2 P.M. no opening occurred during the first day at 15°, the greatest expansion took place at 25°, and in the 20° and 30°

chambers there was little difference other than a delay in opening in the former. In this initial opening there was a direct relation between the degree of expansion and the temperature when the storage period was not extended more than 4 hours into that of daylight. Other experiments not given here in detail showed that the amplitude of movement decreased with the length of the storage period during daylight, so that flowers installed in the chambers at 3 P.M. or later did not open at any temperature during the initial 24 hours. When the closed flowers were removed from the field directly to the ecostat at 5 to 7 A.M. the behavior was entirely like that of the flowers stored during the night. When series were transferred from the field during the day the behavior was strikingly different; full opening and closing occurred at the usual daily period, unless the flowers were cut immediately before the expansion period so that the shock of cutting interfered with the response. Storage under the conditions here employed was unfavorable to floral opening when carried into the daylight period, but more so when the flowers were kept at 15° and 20° than at 25° and 30°.

In the second periodic opening under the constant conditions of the experimental chambers all flowers in the 7 A.M. series at temperatures above 15° expanded to a lower maximum than in their initial opening. At 15° the expansion of the second opening was considerably increased. The percentage second expansion maximum of the first $\left(\dfrac{\text{second maximum}}{\text{first maximum}} \times 100\right)$ in the order of increasing temperatures from 15° were 660, 92, 68, and 85. The flowers of the 7 A.M. series were unique in carrying out a more nearly normal opening during the second period than during the first. Temperatures above 15° were unfavorable for the preparation for opening when applied continuously for 24 hours or more, but were favorable when utilized only during the daylight period. That the higher temperatures did not result in the depletion of the materials necessary for floral movement was shown by the full opening of the cut flowers when placed in the field at the close of the experiment as well as by the fact that the reduction in degree of movement at the second opening did not follow the order of increasing temperature but was 25°, 30°, and 20°, which indicated that 25° was the optimum for this secondary movement.

In the 10 A.M. series the maxima of the second opening exceeded that of the first in every case, indicating that the three hours additional storage beyond that given the 7 A.M. series passed a critical minimum after which further exposure to higher temperatures did not reduce the magnitude of the second expansion. The flowers of the 2 P.M. series showed a second opening greater than the first only at the two lower temperatures. Three hours storage during the day-light period reduced the first opening but favored the second, but **7** hours so disturbed the critical balance that only with further storage at 15° or 20° was the second opening increased.

TABLE 26

MENTZELIA NUDA

Behavior (per cent open) of flowers under constant conditions of darkness, 50% relative humidity, and the temperatures indicated, after varying storage hours.
8 a.m. series: stored 14 hours in Dewar flask.
1 p.m. series: stored 18 hours in Dewar flask.
Changes in temperature are marked with an asterisk.

Temp. °C. Time	15	15-30	15-20	15	15-30	15-20	20	20-30	20-15	20	20-30	20-15	30	30-20	30-15	30	30-20	30-15
8 a.m.	0	0	0	0	2	5	15	7	2	10	5	2	0	7	2	0	0	0
10:30	0	0	0	0	2	5	20	10	5	10	5	2	5	15	2	0	0	0
11:45	0	*0	*0	0	*5	*5	25	*10	*5	15	3	*2	10	*20	*2	0	2	*5
1 p.m.	0	0	0	0	7	5	25	12	5	20	*3	5	10	17	5	0	2	5
2:25	2	0	0	0	7	7	25	17	5	20	5	5	10	17	5	0	6	5
3:20	2	5	5	0	42	10	25	22	7	35	5	5	15	17	5	0	5	5
4:20	5	15	10	0	42	7	30	27	7	35	5	6	20	27	7	82	5	5
5:15	5	12	10	0	42	7	40	42	12	20	25	6	60	50	7	50	5	2
6:50	10	5	7	0	15	7	40	80	12	15	30	6	100	67	5	52	2	2
9	5	2	7	0	10	5	25	85	10		15		100	67	2	52	2	
12 mt.	12	5	2	0		2	15	45	7		12		100	50	2	52		
3 a.m.	10	3	2	0			25	45	7		12		100	40	2			
8:25	10			0			20	45					100	30				
11:45	10			0				40					100	27				

The effects of sudden temperature changes under conditions of 50 per cent relative humidity and darkness was studied in experiments in which freshly cut material was used. Transfers were made between temperatures of 15°, 20°, and 30° at 11:45 A.M. and 3:20 P.M. The average results, together with those of checks held at constant temperatures, are given in Table 26.

Considering first the 8 A.M. series, under constant conditions of 15° there was a slight periodic opening which was not altered in time or degree by a change to 20° at 11:45 A.M., but was slightly increased by the transfer to 30°. In the 1 P.M. series, which had received five hours additional exposure to the conditions of the habitat, similar temperature changes resulted in an increased amplitude of periodic movement. The changes from 15° were not immediately followed by expansion, indicating that there was no stimulating effect but an adjustment of the flowers to the temperature level to which they were transferred.

The behavior of the flowers in the 8 A.M. series changed from 20° to 30° and 15° agrees with that just described. In the 1 P.M. series, changes made at 3:20 P.M. both to 15° and 30° decreased the maximum openings. In this case transfer to a higher temperature did not increase the degree of opening when the change was made late in the preparation period.

Changes from 30° to the lower temperatures reduced the extent of opening markedly both when the changes were made at 11:45 A.M. in the 8 A.M. series, and when they occurred at 3:20 P.M. in the 1 P.M. series. In no case was there a marked closing reaction following the change but a gradual adjustment of the flower to the temperature level. These flowers are not sensitive to sudden changes in temperature in either the opening or closing movement, but show a degree of maximum expansion directly proportional to the temperature.

EFFECTS OF LIGHT

The behavior of the flowers of *Mentzelia nuda* at 20°, 50 per cent relative humidity, and constant levels of .275 and 40 foot-candles light intensity is shown in Table 27. All flowers were brought directly from the field and placed in the experimental chambers at 5 A.M., 12 M., and 3:30 P.M.

In all the series the flowers subjected to the stronger illumination began the periodic opening earlier and expanded to a greater maximum than those in the weaker light. Thus in the 5 A.M. series the flowers under .275 foot-candles light intensity reached the percentage maximum expansion of 22 at 9 P.M., while the comparable set under 40 foot-candles light intensity attained the maximum of 70 at 6 P.M. Similarly the 12 M. series opened to 13 at 7:30 at the lower light intensity, and to 51 at 6 P.M. at the higher. In the 3:30

series maximum openings at the low and high light intensities occurred at 6 P.M., reaching 52 for the lower level and 90 for the higher. It is evident that both the degree of expansion and the time of opening are influenced by the light intensity to which the flowers are exposed.

TABLE 27

MENTZELIA NUDA

Behavior (per cent open) of flowers at 20°C., 50% relative humidity, and constant conditions of .275 and 40 foot-candles light intensity.

Light Intensity (Foot-candles)	.275	40	.275	40	.275	40
Time						
5 a.m	0	0				
9:30	0	0				
12 m.	0	0	0	0		
3 p.m.	0	0	0	0		
3:30	0	5	0	0	0	0
4	0	19	0	7	0	0
5	0	59	0	38	0	27
6	0	70	0	51	52	90
7:30	6	69	13	27	36	48
9	22	55	0	22	15	13
10	22	21	0	21	10	6
11	19	20	0	18	10	0
12 mt.	18	20	0	13	10	0

The effects of changes in illumination between .275 and 40 foot-candles intensities are shown in Table 28. The flowers were brought directly from the field to the experimental chambers and kept at 20° and 50 per cent relative humidity throughout the experiment. All were started at 5 A.M., and the changes in illumination were made at 8 and 11 A.M. and at 4 and 6 P.M. without otherwise disturbing the flowers. To secure accurate comparisons the flowers were shifted simultaneously from low to high and from high to low light intensities.

The maximum openings were greater under the more intense illumination, except in the series in which the change to the higher intensity was made at 6 P.M. after the maximum expansion had already been attained in the comparable set. Thus the maxima openings of the series changed at 8 and 11 A.M. and 4 P.M. were 80, 69, and 21 per cent greater under the more intense illumination than under the weaker. The floral behavior was similar to that which appeared under the influence of sudden changes in temperature. Opening reactions did not follow immediately after the increases in illumination unless these increases occurred at the time for periodic expansion. Thus in the series changed to 40 foot-candles light intensity at 8 and 11 A.M., opening began 10 and 7 hours respectively after the change. At the time for periodic opening similar changes

TABLE 28

MENTZELIA NUDA

Behavior (per cent open) of flowers under constant conditions of 20°C. and 50% relative humidity, and changes between .275 and 40 foot-candles light intensities.

Change in light intensity indicated at head of column is marked with an asterisk.

Light Intensity (Foot-candles)	.275 to 40	40 to .275	.275 to 40	40 to .275	.275 to 40	40 to .275	.275 to 40	40 to .275
Time								
5 a.m.	0	8	0	6	6	5	0	6
8	0*	8*	0	6	6	5	0	6
11	0	8	0*	6*	6	5	0	6
12 m.	0	8	0	6	6	5	0	6
2 p.m.	0	8	0	6	6	5	0	6
3	0	8	0	6	6	5	0	6
4	0	10	0	6	6*	10*	0	8
5	0	11	0	22	8	59	0	84
6	26	11	8	31	11	56	0*	40*
7:30	91	11	100	27	60	37	37	7
9	71	10	100	20	80	30	62	6
10	51	8	45	19	74	28	64	6
11	26	8	21	16	51	25	60	6
12 mt.	17	8	11	16	11	25	47	6

resulted in immediate expansion unless this had already occurred at the time the shift was made. The effect of the more intense light on the degree of expansion is, at least partly, one of light intensity and time. The series shifted at 8 A.M. reached a maximum after 11.5 hours exposure to the more intense illumination, that at 11 A.M. after 8.5 hours, and that at 4 P.M. after 5 hours, the excess expansion over that taking place at the lower intensity being respectively 80, 69, and 21 per cent, as previously mentioned.

The time both of the beginning of the opening movement and of the maximum expansion was later under the more intense light, unless the change in light intensity came when opening was already under way. Comparisons cannot be made with the series shifted at 6 P.M., because opening had occurred before the changes were made. Shifts to 40 foot-candles light intensity at 4 and 6 P.M. initiated the opening reaction and may have acted as a light stimulus to opening, but this view is made doubtful by the delayed response in all other similar changes. Transfer to light of lower intensity affected the closing process only when the change was made at 6 P.M. when closing was already under way.

TISSUE STUDIES

The osmotic concentration of the epidermal cells in the region of maximum curvature of *M. nuda* was determined by the plasmolytic method. Typical curves are shown in Figure 31. The values for the flowers cut at 5 A.M. and held in the chambers at 25°, 50 per cent humidity and darkness are shown by the solid and broken lines; comparative values for flowers at 20° and 40 foot-candles light intensity are shown by the dotted curves. In darkness during the morning the concentration of the cells of the outer epidermis was above that of the inner, but reached equality before noon. During the afternoon there was a marked fall in concentration in the cells on both surfaces but particularly on the outer, bringing the values for this layer below those of the inner. At the time of opening and during the open period the concentrations again rose and crossed, reaching a relation similar to that found in the flowers during the morning period.

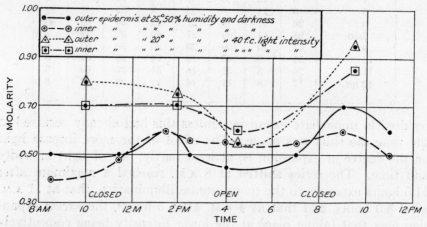

Fig. 31.—Osmotic concentrations of epidermal cells of the petals of *Mentzelia nuda* as determined by the molarity sucrose solution necessary for plasmolysis.

In the comparative series at 15°, the curves for which are not given, the concentrations were slightly above those of the 25° material, but the form of the curves remained similar up to 1 P.M. From that time the values remained approximately equal and constant to the end of the experiment at 10 P.M. During this interval the flowers did not open. The preparation period is thus marked by an increasing concentration in the epidermal cells, and the opening period by a fall in this value, the decline being greater in the outer layer. Closing is characterized by a reverse change toward the original condition. A comparison of the 25° and 15° values indicates that at the latter temperature the processes taking place during the forenoon proceed to a higher maximum than at 25°, but that the fall in concentration accompanying expansion does not occur in the absence of the opening movement.

When flowers were held at 20°, 50 per cent relative humidity, and .275 and 40 foot-candles light intensities, the relative changes in concentration were similar to those described for flowers kept in darkness, but the absolute values were somewhat higher. Curves for flowers under 40 foot-candles light intensity are given in Figure 31. It will be seen that tissue conditions, as reflected by the epidermis, show a period immediately before opening during which the sap concentration is high at the inner surface. This condition is reversed during opening, and again assumes the closed condition of greater concentration in the outer surface than in the inner. The crossing of the concentrations during the opening period is delayed by exposure to light in the same way as the opening movements.

The movement of flowers of *M. nuda* is conditioned by a differential osmotic concentration in the epidermal cells, but the changes in concentration and the consequent movement are probably brought about by hydration phenomena.

MENTZELIA MULTIFLORA
FIELD BEHAVIOR

Mentzelia multiflora occurs on open gravel slopes in the Pike's Peak region at 6000 to 11,000 feet elevation. The yellow flowers are produced in numbers on long flexible branches from June to September. The floral history is shown in Plate 21. The sticky calyx lobes are forced apart by the growing cone of the corolla and are gradually reflexed, reaching the complete and permanent recurved position after 24 hours. The first opening of the corolla occurs from 3 to 5 P.M., 1 to 4 days after the reflexion of the calyx, the movement requiring about 30 minutes. The flowers usually remain open 2 to 4 hours, depending on weather conditions. The opening and closing movements are repeated on 3 to 5 successive days. During warm humid weather the flowers may remain open throughout the night. When a sudden and extreme fall in temperature occurs during the open period, closing movements may be checked so that the flowers remain partly open throughout the night or even the following day. The field behavior of *Mentzelia multiflora* is strikingly variable and could not be correlated with factor measurements made at or near the time of the opening and closing periods.

FIELD EXPERIMENTS

Uncut flowers were enclosed in bell jars in the habitat, and were heated or cooled by coils through which brine of the desired temperature was circulated, and subjected to moist or dry air and to different degrees of shading. Checks were maintained both in bell jars with the habitat factors otherwise unchanged, and unenclosed. Flowers enclosed in the early afternoon when the air temperature was 20° to 25° and kept at 30° and at 20° in air 40 per cent saturated with water vapor, opened at the same time as the adjacent free checks. Flowers at 30° remained open to the end of the experiment at 12 midnight when the air temperature had decreased to 8° to 10°, and the free and enclosed checks had closed at 9 P.M. At 20°, opening occurred at the time at which it took place in the checks; but closing, though delayed, was in progress at midnight. The removal of the bell jars resulted in the closing of the flowers which had been heated to 30° and 20°, and all behaved normally on the following day. Flowers similarly cooled to 15° opened and closed with the checks. Shading and high humidities applied during the afternoon produced no change in the time of opening. If these factors are of importance in the field it is rather during the preparation period than during the time at which movement is in progress.

The removal of some of the petals either when the flower was open or closed did not alter the behavior of the remaining parts. Dis-

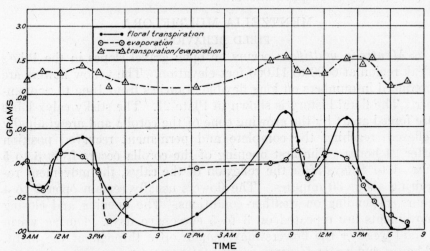

Fig. 32.—Average hourly transpiration of flowers of *Mentzelia multiflora*, and evaporation per square centimeter free water surface.

secting the sepals from the bud did not affect the subsequent opening, although such mutilated flowers frequently collapsed prematurely. The transpiration relations of flowers were studied by cutting under

Flower cycle of *Mentzelia multiflora*

water those which had passed through one open period, and exposing them in sealed vials held in an upright position at flower level by placing in blackened wood blocks. Evaporation from a free water surface was determined by exposing at flower level a blackened pan 10 cm. in diameter and 7 mm. deep, in which water was kept at a depth of 5 mm. Transpiration and evaporation were determined by weighing. The average transpiration and evaporation values followed a similar daily cycle, rising during the day and falling at night, but in no case was there any apparent effect on the transpiration-evaporation ratio that could be attributed to the opening and closing of the flowers. Figure 32 gives the curves.

Since the stomata are apparently inactive in this flower, and transpiration is cuticular, it is difficult to see how the position of the petals could be without effect on the water loss. The method here used was probably not sufficiently accurate to detect the transpirational effects of opening and closing.

LABORATORY EXPERIMENTS

Table 29 gives the percentage opening of flowers of *M. multiflora* under constant conditions of 30° and 20° temperature, 50 per cent relative humidity, and .275 foot-candles light intensity. It will be seen that in flowers taken directly from the field to the experimental chambers at 3-hour intervals from 3 A.M. to 3 P.M., periodic movements occurred in every case. Neither the time of removal from the field nor the temperatures of 20° and 30° altered significantly the time at which the maximum expansion was reached, this usually being from 6 to 7 P.M.

PERIODICITY

At 30° there was no change in the rate of opening proportional to the duration of the series—that is, length of field exposure during the day—but at 20° there was a progressive increase. The values are shown under the heading "No Storage," in Table 32, which also gives the opening rates for flowers placed under experimental conditions at 6 P.M. when the opening movement was already in progress. Since field temperatures were 22° to 27°, the transfer to the 20° chamber was a reduction in temperature, so that the sudden change could not account for the increasing rate of opening with the duration of the series. At 30° the preparation for opening went on in the experimental chambers so that the rates did not increase with increasing field exposure, but that conditions in the field were more favorable than those in the 30° chamber is shown by the high rate of the 6 P.M. series. It seems evident that there is a preparation period for opening, for which the day exposure to field conditions or to those of the 30° chamber is favorable in proportion to its duration.

The results for the comparable series in the 10° chamber are omitted in all the work on *Mentzelia multiflora*, because no opening movements occurred at this temperature; as in the case of *M. nuda*,

TABLE 29
MENTZELIA MULTIFLORA
Behavior (per cent open) of flowers under constant conditions of 30° and 20°, 50% relative humidity, and .275 foot-candles light intensity.

Temp. °C.	30					20				
Time										
3 a.m.	0					0				
4	0					0				
5	0					0				
6	0	0				0	0			
7	0	0				0	0			
8	0	0				0	0			
9	0	0	0			0	0	0		
10	0	0	0			0	0	0		
11	0	0	0			0	0	0		
12 m.	0	0	0	0		0	0	0	0	
1 p.m.	0	0	0	0		5	0	0	0	
2	0	0	0	0		5	0	0	0	
3	0	0	0	0	0	13	0	0	0	0
4	33	15	0	3	45	23	0	0	0	0
5	95	62	5	64	88	37	1	23	23	25
6	100	89	81	98	100	52	19	69	68	92
7	100	93	98	98	100	44	35	72	59	90
8	95	92	93	93	100	23	52	60	36	15
9	82	74	93	74	100	23	35	42	16	9
10	82	71	89	63	95	23	20	15	7	3
11	81	62	73	41	93	23	17	13	0	3
12 mt.	80	53	65	35	88	23	8	9	0	3
1 a.m.	80	46	62	32	84	23	6	9	0	2
2	80	43	59	27	80	23	4	7	0	1
3	80	33	55	23	75	23	4	7	0	0
4	80	33	55	22	75	23	3	6	0	0
5	80	33	55	22	75	23	3	5	0	0
6	80	33	55	22	75	23	3	4	0	0
7	80	33	55	21	75	23	3	4	0	0
8	80	33	55	21	75	23	3	4	0	0

all periodic movements were checked. At 20° and 30° all flowers showed closing movements, but these were slight after long exposure in the 30° chamber.

The flowers used in experiments the results of which are summarized in Table 30 received storage periods varying from 3 to 48

TABLE 30

MENTZELIA MULTIFLORA

Behavior (per cent open) of flowers at 30° and 20°, 50% relative humidity, and 275 foot-candles light intensity, after night storage periods at 10°, 100% humidity, and darkness.

Temp. °C	30						20					
Cutting Time	3 a.m.	12 mt.	9 p.m.	6 p.m.	6 a.m.	6 a.m.	3 a.m.	12 mt.	9 p.m.	9 p.m.	6 a.m.	6 a.m.
Night Storage (Hours)	3	6	9	12	24	48	3	6	9	12	24	48
Time												
6 a.m.	0	0	0	0	0	0	0	0	0	0	0	0
7	0	0	0	0	0	0	0	0	0	0	0	0
8	0	0	0	0	0	0	0	0	0	0	0	0
9	0	0	0	0	0	0	0	0	0	0	0	0
10	0	0	0	0	0	0	0	0	0	0	0	0
11	3	5	5	5	5	0	0	0	0	0	0	0
12 m.	50	25	70	25	5	5	0	0	0	0	0	0
1 p.m.	95	53	93	71	70	25	0	0	3	0	0	0
2	98	98	100	92	93	80	10	5	3	5	0	0
3	98	100	100	100	100	90	50	50	38	12	5	3
4	98	100	90	100	100	100	80	93	43	55	70	40
5	85	98	75	88	88	100	70	75	88	97	95	55
6	58	93	50	70	88	75	35	45	100	62	35	95
7	58	85	45	46	88	50	20	23	20	20	25	85
8	58	85	45	45	88	50	18	23	3	7	25	63
9	58	85	45	45	88	45	10	23	3	0	0	23
10	58	85	45	45	88	45	4	18	3	0	0	5
11	58	85	45	45		45	0	7	0	0		5
12 mt.								5	0			5
1 a.m.									0			5

hours after removal from the field. In all cases this material was installed in the experimental chambers at 6 A.M., so that all of the storage period, or the final part of it, was during the night period. Periodic opening and closing appeared in every case, the closing movements, like those in the unstored material, being limited in extent at 30°. The time at which the maximum expansion was attained showed an insignificant advance, being from 5 to 6 P.M. The opening rates computed from the values in Table 30 are given under the heading "Night Storage," in Table 32. Little more than variation was shown by the flowers in the 30° chamber, there being no significant disturbance in the periodic behavior. The percentage average opening for all material after night storage periods was 21.8 as against 23.2 for unstored material. In the 20° chamber the opening of the stored material, though variable, showed a distinctly higher rate than did the unstored, the average values being 23.7 and 13 respectively. In the 10° chamber no movement occurred.

Night storage under the conditions here employed did not disturb the periodic behavior of the flowers but accelerated the rate of opening at 20°. As judged by the rates of opening, exposure during the night to field conditions, and to 10°, 50 per cent humidity, and darkness, is equally effective when the day period is passed at 30°; but when the same night treatment is followed by the subjection of the flowers to 20°, the 10° storage is more favorable.

Table 31 shows the results for flowers stored under conditions identical with those governing experiments recorded in Table 30, except that the storage periods were given during the daylight instead of the night hours. All the flowers were removed from the field at 6 A.M. and subjected to the storage conditions for a portion of the day before being placed in the experimental chambers. These flowers showed a greatly disturbed periodicity, the times at which the maximum openings were attained varying widely. In the 30° chamber the flowers subjected to 3 hours storage and brought to the experimental chambers at 9 A.M. showed little disturbance in rhythm, opening to full expansion at 5 P.M. In the series installed in the chambers at 12 M., 3 P.M., and 6 P.M., after 6, 9, and 12 hours storage, these maxima occurred at 8 P.M. and 12 midnight. In the 20° chamber the maximum openings were at 9 P.M., 10 P.M., 2 A.M., and 3 A.M., for the series in the order given. No movement took place at 10°.

The results given in Table 31 show not only a delay in the time of the maximum opening of flowers subjected to storage during the daylight period, but also a reduction in the rate of opening. That is, the time of the beginning of the opening movement was not as greatly retarded by the storage periods as the time at which the maximum opening occurred.

The opening rates are given under the heading "Day Storage," in Table 32, and show variable results in the 30° chamber, the values being high in the flowers receiving 3 and 12 hours storage. The average rate for all storage periods for flowers in the 30° chamber

TABLE 31

MENTZELIA MULTIFLORA

Behavior (per cent open) of flowers at 30° and 20°C., 50% relative humidity, and .275 foot-candles light intensity, after day storage periods at 10°, 100% humidity, and darkness, following removal from the field at 6 a.m.

Temp. °C.	30				20			
Day Storage (Hours)	3	6	9	12	3	6	9	12
Time								
9 a.m.	0				0			
10	0				0			
11	0				0			
12 m.	0	0			0	0		
1 p.m.	0	0			0	0		
2	0	0			0	0		
3	0	0	0		0	0	0	
4	5	2	0		0	0	0	
5	100	50	0		0	1	0	
6	100	52	0	0	1	4	0	0
7	100	90	4	0	24	13	5	0
8	100	92	24	0	52	14	14	2
9	100	92	28	0	53	33	15	6
10	100	88	43	63	42	53	15	7
11	100	76	49	75	38	35	15	11
12 mt.	88	70	77	90	22	33	15	14
1 a.m.	86	61	74	90	16	32	15	14
2	75	52	60	90	9	27	20	14
3	75	43	47	85	6	20	19	28
4	75	42	47	85	2	13	11	28
5	75	41	47	85	2	6	4	28
6	75	40	47	80	2	4	4	15
7	75	40	47	80	2	4	4	15
8	75	40	47	80	2	4	4	15

was 28.9, as compared to 32.6 for the 9 A.M. series receiving no storage. At 20°, where periodic effects are less obscured, the opening rates declined markedly, ranging from 14.2 to 2.5 and showing an average of 7 as compared with 24 for flowers with no storage.

In experiments the results of which are not detailed here, the storage period of cut flowers was increased to 153 hours, the series being installed at 3 P.M. so that the greater part of the daylight period was included. At 20° the time of the maximum opening was delayed and the degree of expansion and the opening rate reduced, but to no greater extent than was shown by flowers which had been subjected to day storage of 9 and 12 hours. The effects of storage at 10°, 100 per cent humidity, and darkness, on the periodic opening, are exerted during the daylight period which immediately precedes floral expansion.

EFFECTS OF TEMPERATURE

The behavior of the flowers of *M. multiflora* brought directly from the field to the chambers shows a direct response to the temperature levels at which they were held (Table 29). It will be seen that in these flowers the degree of maximum expansion varied directly with temperature. Including the values obtained at 10°—which are not tabulated because they were invariably zero—and those at 25°, the

TABLE 32

MENTZELIA MULTIFLORA

Rate of opening of flowers under constant conditions of 30°C., 50% humidity, and .275 foot-candles light intensity.

Starting Time	No Storage	Night Storage (Hours)						Day Storage (Hours)			
		3	6	9	12	24	48	3	6	9	12
3 a.m.	33.3										
6	23.2	24.5	20	25	20	20	20				
9	32.6							50			
12 m.	32.6								23		
3 p.m.	33.3									12.8	
6	75										30
3 a.m.	8.6										
6	13	26.6	31	16.6	24.2	31.6	23.7				
9	24							14.2			
12 m.	34								8.8		
3 p.m.	45.5									2.5	
6	70										3.5

average percentage openings for the flowers at 10°, 20°, 25°, and 30°, were 0, 67, 74, and 98. The closing process exhibits great variability but a general inverse relation to the temperature. At 10° the flowers remained closed, at 20° approximately complete closure followed the open period except in the 3 A.M. series, and at 30° closure was variable and incomplete, the average percentage minimum openings at 10°, 20°, and 30°, being respectively 0, 6, and 51.

The results for flowers which received various periods of night storage (Table 30), exhibit a different relation. The percentage maxima of the 6 A.M. series, receiving no storage (Table 29), were 52 and 93 at 20° and 30° respectively, or at 20° the flowers opened to 55.9 per cent, the maximum expansion attained at 30°. Comparative values—that is, percentage maximum opening at 20° compared with that at 30°—for 3, 6, 9, 12, 24, and 48 hours storage were respectively 89, 93, 100, 97, 95, and 95. With night storage at 10°, 100 per cent humidity, and darkness, the difference between maximum expansions at 30° and 20° was greatly reduced, the degree of reduction being approximately equal in flowers stored from 3 to 48 hours. The relation of floral expansion to temperature is dependent on the temperature of the preparation period quite as much as on that obtaining at the time expansion takes place, but there is a critical balance which is passed with 3 hours storage, after which additional storage makes little difference in the degree of expansion. The relative values of the minimum openings to which closure extended at 20° and 30° with and without storage were variable. The average percentage minima to which the stored material closed were 61 and 1.6 for 30° and 20°, compared to 33 and 3 for the unstored.

When the flowers received storage during the day the openings did not vary consistently with the length of the storage period but showed a marked reduction at 20° compared with that at 30°, the average percentage values being approximately 39 and 90, giving a ratio of 43. The minimum percentage values to which closure proceeded were 6 and 60 for 20° and 30°.

The opening rates given in Table 32 show that flowers subjected to no storage opened at a greater rate at 30° than at 20° only in the forenoon series. The difference in the opening rates decreased as the time of removal from the field approached noon, after which a critical balance was passed so that the opening rates at 20° became as much as or more than those at 30°. Storage during the day increased the difference between the 30° and 20° rates, the averages for all storage periods being approximately 29 and 9.7 for 30° and 20°.

Sudden shifts in temperature between 10°, 20°, and 30° produced no immediate change in movement. If periodic opening was under way when a change to a higher temperature was made, floral behavior was altered only to that of the temperature level obtaining at the time. There appeared to be no stimulatory action due to the change.

It is apparent from the results given that the temperature relations of *Mentzelia multiflora* are not simple and must be interpreted in the light of conditions during the preparation period while the flowers are in the closed condition, as well as of those obtaining at the time of floral movement. In these experiments the preparation period does not show a simple time-temperature relation, but rather a point of critical balance after which little effect is observable. Flowers may show a direct or inverse relation between maximum expansion and temperature according to the period of the day at which they have been subjected to conditions of 10° and darkness. The rate of expansion and time of maximum opening may show similar relations, or the flowers may appear entirely insensitive to all temperature changes within the limits permitting floral activity.

EFFECTS OF LIGHT AND HUMIDITY

Experiments on the flowers of *M. multiflora* with .275 and 40 foot-candles light intensity were carried out along the lines of the work with *Mentzelia nuda*, with like results. At 20° and 50 per cent humidity the flowers responded to light of the higher intensity by maintaining a greater degree of expansion during the open period. Details of these experiments will not be given here because of their similarity to those already discussed.

Experiments were carried out at 20° and darkness to test any differences in floral behavior at 75 and 25 per cent relative humidity. No significant differences could be found, the floral movements not being affected by these humidities when applied at or near the opening period.

TISSUE STUDIES

The tissue mechanism of *M. multiflora* seemed much like that described for *M. nuda*. Both the petals and filaments carried out repeated opening and closing movements, but the sepals, being inactive after the first opening, were not studied. The osmotic concentrations in the epidermal cells on the opposite surfaces of the regions of maximum curvature were found to be lowest in the young bud, and highest in the flowers which had been open several times but were not yet collapsed. In the buds the values were about .3 molar as determined by plasmolysis with sucrose solution at 20°. When closed, flowers which had passed through one open period gave concentrations of .4 and .45 for outer and inner epidermis respectively; during opening these values rose to equality at .6, and during the closing period maintained equal values, falling to .5.

When a portion of the receptacle bearing floral parts was immersed in distilled water at 25°, the petals bent inward, finally coming to rest at 80 degrees from the line of the peduncle; that is, they were in a closed position which would be impossible when the petals were opposing each other from the various sides of the receptacle. When sucrose solutions of increasing concentration were used instead of water, the petals curved outward. In .1 molar the angle inward was 40 degrees, in .2 molar the petals curved outward at 40 degrees, and in .5 molar to 80 degrees, which is approximately the full open position.

SUMMARY

When brought from the field and placed under constant conditions of temperature, light and humidity, all *Mentzelia* flowers exhibit a daily periodic cycle of movement, opening in the late afternoon. The time of these periodic movements is not altered by different constant temperatures between 15° and 30°, by illumination of different intensities within the range tried, by different times of removal from the field, nor by exposure to constant conditions of 50 per cent relative humidity, .275 foot-candles light intensity, and 20°, 25°, and 30° temperature for periods up to 30 hours. Night storage at 10°, 100 per cent humidity, and darkness increases the amplitude of the succeeding periodic movement, but day storage under these conditions results in a variable response of decreased amplitude and disturbs the time of periodic opening. Night storage increases the rate of opening on the following day, but day storage decreases it, and to an equal degree at all periods greater than 3 hours. Storage for different periods of 24 hours or more has the same effect on floral behavior as that of treatment for the final day or night period of the longer exposure. Under constant conditions of light, humidity, and temperatures of 15° to 30°, periodic opening and closing occur on the second day, but with decreased amplitude of movement at the higher temperatures, and increased at the lower.

Maximum floral expansions are proportional to the temperatures from 15° to 30°, unless the flowers have been stored during the day at low temperatures and darkness. All floral movements are checked at 10°. Subjection to conditions in the 30° chamber or long exposure at 25° and 20° prevents complete closure. Exposure of uncut flowers in the field during the night, and storage of cut flowers during this period at 10° and darkness, result in similar floral behavior on the next day. Storage until 10 A.M. passes a critical balance, after which the extent of opening during the first day is reduced but that of the second increased. Sudden changes in temperature between 10° and 30° do not produce immediate responses and probably cannot be regarded as stimulatory. Light delays the time but increases the degree of maximum expansion in proportion to its intensity.

There is a daily cycle of change in the osmotic concentration of the epidermal cells which shows a fall during floral opening and probably indicates an increase in water content of the active tissues during this movement. Opening and closing movements may be induced in petals by immersion in .5 molar sucrose solution and in water. Flower movements in *Mentzelia* are to be connected with the water content of the tissues in the region of curvature. Such changes may be due to alterations in the osmotic activity of the solutes, or to cell permeability, but the resulting adjustments of water content are probably between tissues rather than between organs of the plant.

SILENE NOCTIFLORA

The floral history of *Silene noctiflora* is shown in Plate 22. The first opening of the bud is preceded by a rapid elongation of the corolla, which unrolls late in the afternoon while the petals are still curved longitudinally (Plate 22, 6 P.M. stage). As the petals flatten they bend outward to full opening. Unlike *Mentzelia nuda* and *M. multiflora,* these flowers remain open regularly throughout the night and open on two successive days. Like *Mentzelia,* they are nyctanthous and show similar relations under controlled conditions.

Flower cycle of *Silene noctiflora*

IX
EPHEMERAL NYCTANTHOUS FLOWERS
FIELD BEHAVIOR

The various species of *Oenothera* and of related genera are similar in floral mechanism and behavior and will be considered as a group, the specific differences being noted. The following forms were studied in some detail: *Oenothera albicaulis, O. biennis, O. caespitosa, O. coronopifolia, O. drummondi, O. lamarckiana, O. missouriensis, O. pallida, O. rosea, O. spiralis, O. trichocalyx, Gaura coccinea, G. parviflora.*

The immature buds of *Oenothera lamarckiana* are directed downward but assume an upright position on the day preceding opening. During the afternoon of the day on which opening occurs the buds swell noticeably and become yellowish green. The tips of the sepals are spread slightly, exposing the end of the corolla cone and the stigma (Plate 23, 4 P.M. stage). The bases of the sepals gradually spring outward, cracking apart in this region and separating along a single line for the entire length of the bud. The corolla is under tension and immediately unrolls against the restraining calyx (Plate 23, 6 P.M. stage). The movements which follow occur very rapidly. The sepals spring downward as the corolla unrolls and turn back along the tubular portion of the flower, the final movement being sudden. These phases are shown in Plate 23, the 6:15 P.M. to the 6:55 P.M. stages. The lobes of the corolla expand at once, and the stamens with their viscous threads of sticky pollen spread for the reception of sphingid moth visitors (Plate 23, 6:57 P.M. stage). After the initial separation of the calyx the entire opening process requires less than an hour. The flowers remain fresh during the night and usually collapse during the morning, the time varying with the severity of the desiccation conditions.

An opening process similar in movement and time to that of *O. lamarckiana* occurs in *O. biennis,* a common native species found up to 11,000 feet elevation. Many buds of this species fail to open because of the larva of a moth which destroys the interior. Although these buds enlarge, they do not open, but they set abundant seed, the larva rupturing the anthers before destroying the stigma and style and thus effecting self pollination. During dry periods many buds which are not infected do not open, the sepals being so firmly attached that they resist separation. Buds in this condition will not open when the plant is irrigated or when cut and placed in water, unless the sepals are artificially separated when the petals demonstrate a normal tension by springing to a partly open position.

Oenothera caespitosa is common on gravel slopes from 6000 to 9000 feet elevation, the large white flowers being produced on short erect peduncles throughout the summer. Plate 24 shows successive views of a group from a single camera position. During either the day on which opening occurs, or the preceding day, the growing corolla cone forces the sepals apart. The stigma may or may not be exerted. During this condition the heavy midrib and incurved edges of the sepals hold them rigid against the corolla so that considerable force is necessary to reflex them. The sepals are slowly spread, allowing the petals to unroll to an angle of about 45 degrees, and are then quickly reflexed. The corolla, released by this movement, immediately expands. Collapse follows with the arrival of the severe desiccating conditions of the morning.

Societies of *O. albicaulis* are common in the plains region about Colorado Springs. During the flowering season in May and June these societies are conspicuous when in the evening many hundreds of the gleaming white flowers are suddenly unfurled. The sepals of this species remain attached at the tips and prevent the opening of the flower until separated by the pressure from the corolla. The sepals crack apart at the base and spring out, drawing toward the base of the flower the tube composed of the adhering tips. As the calyx is drawn down, the corolla spreads, forming a cone of increasing angle with the apex at the base of the flower, so that the rate of withdrawal of the calyx is increased with the progress of opening. As the calyx ring approaches the base, the petals expand with increasing rapidity because each withdrawal permits a greater expansion of the corolla the nearer to the base of the flower the restraining tips are forced. The result on floral opening is that the process begins slowly but proceeds with increasing speed, an inconspicuous bud spreading into a showy flower in as short a time as 20 seconds. The calyx is usually wholly separated into two groups by the time expansion is complete. Stages in the opening process are shown in Plate 25. There is great activity among the visiting insects at the opening period. Moths may be seen hovering about, and crepuscular bees visiting the buds and trying to force an entrance through the corolla, thus hastening the initial opening movements. Plate 25 shows a common sphingid moth at the open flower.

The opening process of *O. albicaulis* is typical of that of most of the native species, and of *O. rosea*, shown in Plate 26. This species, and also *O. contorta*, opens from 6 to 7:30 A.M., and collapses in the afternoon during the cooler portion of the flowering season.

Flower cycle of *Oenothera lamarckiana*

Oenothera coronopifolia frequently occurs in the habitat with *O. albicaulis,* but the flowering season is later and the size of the flower and plant smaller. Opening is not as rapid as that of *O. albicaulis,* but requires about 30 minutes. The calyx splits into two groups, exposing the short petals with the stigma and anthers projecting. The flowers may remain in this condition from 3 minutes to 1 hour. The four sepals then split apart and are reflexed singly at irregular intervals by a rapid movement requiring 1 to 2 minutes. The slowly spreading corolla does not touch the sepals, and the expansion is not restricted by them.

FIELD EXPERIMENTS

Experiments with *O. caespitosa* were not satisfactory because of the uncertainty of selecting buds at definite intervals before opening. Both the immature and mature buds are erect and often remain with sepals spread and stigma exerted for two days before opening. Field measurements to determine the growth of the bud failed to show a distinctive period immediately preceding opening. Failure to open was thus of uncertain meaning, a fact that made this species unsatisfactory for laboratory experimentation as well as for field studies.

Buds enclosed in bell jars heated to 30° failed to open by 8 P.M. when adjacent checks opened at 6:30, but expanded within 30 minutes after the removal of the jars, the air temperature being 10° to 12°. In similar experiments it was found possible to prevent opening by maintaining constant conditions of 30° and 65 per cent humidity, and to cause opening by reducing the temperature to 10° at 8 P.M.

Although many erect buds of *O. biennis* failed to open during dry weather, irrigation of the plants made no apparent change. That connection with the plant was not necessary for the opening of mature buds of *O. albicaulis* was shown by the fact that when cut at 5 P.M. and left in the field both with and without a water supply the flowers opened at 6:30 P.M. simultaneously with those undisturbed. The water content was not appreciably greater at the time of opening than in the closed buds. Heating or cooling the buds enclosed in bell jars was without effect on the time of opening. *Oenothera albicaulis* appeared to have a much stronger periodicity than did *O. caespitosa* or *O. biennis.*

Experiments to determine the evaporation rate from flowers in the open and closed condition failed to show any distinct effect of opening. The total transpiration from a flower of *O. albicaulis* during the open period, 6 P.M. to 6 A.M., was very small, averaging

.4 cc per flower, or about one-fifth the evaporation per square centimeter of free water surface exposed at flower level. Determinations during the morning period of floral collapse showed that the transpiration-evaporation ratio at this time was also low. Collapse of the flowers is apparently due to a low rate of water supply rather than to a large increase in the transpiration rate.

LABORATORY EXPERIMENTS

Ecostat experiments with the flowers of *O. lamarckiana* showed that at 50 per cent relative humidity and darkness the time of reaching maximum expansion was not different at 15° and 25°, full opening being attained at the time for its periodic appearance in the field. The degree of maximum expansion varied directly with the temperature, being 100 per cent at 25°, and 11 per cent at 15°. The opening rates varied with the temperature, being 21 and 7 at 25° and 15° respectively.

Buds placed in the ecostat chambers at 4 A.M. at 25°, 50 per cent relative humidity, and 40 and .275 foot-candles light intensities, opened to similar maxima, 94 and 91 per cent respectively. The flowers under the more intense illumination reached maximum expansion earlier than those under the less intense light. The rate of opening was quicker under the more intense illumination, but the degree of opening showed great variation. After 18 hours storage at 10°, 100 per cent humidity, and darkness, the degrees and rates of opening were similar at 15°, 20°, and 30°.

TISSUE STUDIES

Studies by the plasmolytic method failed to show any consistent difference in concentration between the cells of the epidermis on the opposite surfaces of the sepals of any of the *Oenothera* species. Since the sepals could be caused to take the open or closed position by immersion in water or in .5 molar sucrose solution, the water relations are probably closely connected with movement. With the mass of tissue present in the regions of curvature of this organ it is probable that the epidermis is effective only indirectly in reducing the rate of water loss, and not directly in producing movement. The fact that the plasmolytic values in the cells of the epidermis were increased from .35 to .40 by exposure to light, and that opening was limited in continued darkness during the daylight period, indicates that the concentration in the cells of the epidermis is closely related to habitat factors and increased with floral activity. In the field the concentrations were low in the bud and in the collapsed flower, and high during the active life of this structure.

Flower cycle of *Oenothera caespitosa*

Flower cycle of *Oenothera albicaulis*

5 P.M.

5.30 P.M.

5.40 P.M.

5.45 P.M.

Flower cycle of *Oenothera rosea*

In the petals, which also can be caused to assume the closed or open position by immersion in water or in .5 molar sucrose solution, the epidermis constitutes a much greater proportion of the tissues. Here changes in turgescence of the epidermal cells can readily be considered directly effective in floral movement. Studies of *O. caespitosa, O. biennis,* and *O. albicaulis* showed the concentrations on opposite surfaces equal and low in the bud, greater and high on the inner surface just preceding and at the time of opening, and equal and low in the collapsing flower. During the opening process, extreme concentrations in *O. biennis* were .75 molar in the cells of the outer epidermis, and 1.30 molar in those of the inner.

MIRABILIS JALAPA

The flowers of *Mirabilis jalapa* open from 5:30 to 6:30 P.M., the process requiring 15 to 30 minutes, and collapse the following forenoon with the arrival of the more severe desiccating conditions. Various stages in the floral life-history are shown in Plate 27. During the morning of the day on which opening occurs, the petals enlarge and at 5 to 6 P.M. are bulged out from the attached margins of the corolla lobes (Plate 27, 5 P.M. and 5:15 P.M. stages). As these separate, the corolla opens to full expansion and the stamens spread apart. The calyx remains inactive.

LABORATORY EXPERIMENTS

Table 33 gives the percentage opening of flowers of *Mirabilis jalapa* under the constant conditions of temperature, light, and relative humidity listed at the head of the columns. There was a periodic opening under all conditions tried, except at 15° and with long exposure to 30°. Although a maximum was reached at a later time in the experimental chambers than is usual in the field, this time was not significantly altered at temperatures of 20°, 25°, and 30°. At 20° the time of the periodic opening was not changed notably by the time of removal from the field, but was delayed by exposure to the light intensities tried, and was advanced slightly by high humidity.

At 30° the time of the initiation of the periodic opening was greatly affected by the time of removal from the field. In this case the predetermined power of movement is apparently increased by conditions in the habitat, at least up to 2 P.M., and to some degree between 2 and 4 P.M. Further, a superoptimal temperature seems to counteract or suppress this increasing movement potential. It was not determined what forces were in play here, but it can safely be assumed that a metabolic balance is basic. Whether this balance lies in chemical, physical, or vital phenomena is an open question, but the results of the tissue studies seem to indicate that chemical changes could not be responsible.

TABLE 33

Mirabilis Jalapa

Behavior (per cent open) of flowers under various constant conditions of temperature, light, and humidity.

Light Conditions (Foot-candles)	Darkness												.275	40	Darkness	
Humidity %	50												50		20	75
Temp. °C	15	20	20	20	20	20	25	30	30	30	30	30	25		25	
Time																
4:30 a.m.													0	0		
5		0					0						0	0		
6		0					0						0	0	0	0
7	0	0					0						0	0	0	0
8	0	0					0	0					0	0	0	0
9	0	0					0	0					0	0	0	0
10	0	0	0				0	0	0				0	0	0	0
11	0	0	0				0	0	0				0	0	0	0
12 m.	0	0	0	0			0	0	0	0			0	0	0	0
1 p.m.	0	0	0	0			0	0	0	0			0	0	0	0
2	0	0	0	0	0		0	0	0	0	0		0	0	0	0
3	0	0	0	0	0		0	0	0	0	0		0	0	0	0
4	0	0	0	0	0		0	0	0	0	0		0	10	15	7
4:30	0	26	0	0	11	0	0	0	0	0	0	0	3	34	40	17
5	0	37	0	0	12	15	29	0	0	0	0	22	25	43	58	37
5:30	0	49	8	12	17	23	55	0	0	0	0	35	40	45	62	53
6	0	59	42	47	34	60	65	0	0	0	0	43	55	47	63	70
6:30	0	67	47	48	45	65	75	0	0	0	0	55	68	60	74	70
7	0	75	53	49	56	72	80	0	0	0	0	60	83	79	76	70
7:30	0	80	58	50	72	78	87	0	0	0	0	68	90	88	76	71
8	0	85	69	52	80	85	100	0	0	0	59	78	91	93	78	71
8:30	0	87	70	65	82	85	100	0	0	0	93	80	97	93	77	71
9	0	92	73	80	86	83	100	0	0	0	97	82	97	95	78	71
10	0	87	94	80	85	84	100	0	0	0	87	84	90	95	78	71
11	0	87	94	80	85	84	100	0	0	0	87	84	90	95	78	71

The degree of maximum expansion did not vary directly with the temperature but was greatest at 25°, darkness, and 50 per cent relative humidity, which appeared to be near the optimum. The degree of maximum opening was slightly reduced by the light intensities tried, and also by humidities of 20 and 75 per cent as compared to 50 per cent. The opening rates increased with the temperature up to 25°, but fell at 30°, the average values for the temperatures from 15° to 30° being 0, 20, 29, and 10. The opening rates at 25° were reduced by .275 and 40 foot-candles light intensity,

Flower cycle of *Mirabilis jalapa*

the values for darkness and the two intensities in the order given being 29, 22, and 16, respectively. In darkness all opening movements were prevented by temperatures of 15°, and by long exposure during the daylight period to 30°.

TISSUE STUDIES

Since the veins of the corolla are comparatively rigid and the greater part of the movement occurs in the intervascular region, epidermis from this part of *Mirabilis jalapa* was used for the values shown in Figure 33. The flowers were removed from the field at 2 A.M. and placed under constant conditions of 20°, 50 per cent humidity, and .275 and 40 foot-candles light intensity.

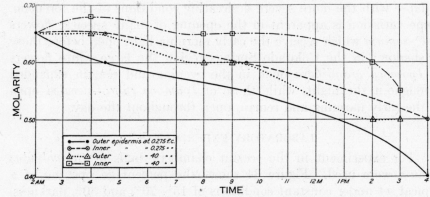

FIG. 33.—Osmotic concentrations of epidermal cells of the petals of flowers of *Mirabilis jalapa* under constant conditions of 20° C. and 50 per cent humidity, and light intensities of .275 and 40 foot-candles

In general the cells from flowers at both intensities showed a decreasing concentration during the day. The values at the more intense illumination remained higher than those at the less intense, even showing a slight initial rise. All cells contained starch which decreased during the day and disappeared from the collapsed flower. There seemed to be a simultaneous hydrolysis of starch in the cells and a fall in osmotic pressure during the preparation period. Although there was an evident enlargement of the bud on the day of its opening, the water relations of the tissues are probably the effective mechanism involved in floral opening. Opening movements occur from the higher toward the lower concentration, closure resulting from collapse beginning in the marginal area.

CONVOLVULUS AND IPOMOEA

Convolvulus arvensis and *C. sepium* are plentiful in waste places about Colorado Springs, and various species of *Convolvulus* and

Ipomoea are commonly cultivated. Although there is a wide variation in the time of movement in the various species, the mechanism involved seems similar. Plate 28 shows stages in the floral life-history of *Ipomoea purpurea.* preceding the opening the buds enlarge rapidly, the outer half of the corolla being tightly rolled. About 1 hour before the full opening the corolla unrolls and appears with the intervascular region folded inward (Plate 28, 3, 3:20, and 3:30 A.M. stages). The entire marginal area then curves out, straightening the folds and bringing the flower fully open (Plate 28, 3:40 and 3:50 A.M. stages). In closing, the marginal areas collapse before the vascular regions (Plate 28, 10 and 11 A.M. stages).

In most species opening occurs in the early morning, and collapse with the more severe desiccating conditions of the forenoon. Some variation is apparent in the opening of many species; flowers of *C. sepium* which receive the early morning light open before those in shadow; in the Colorado Springs region the large white flowers of *Ipomoea grandiflora* open in the evening and remain expanded throughout the night, while those of *Ipomoea rubro-coerulea* open in the early morning and remain open throughout the day.

LABORATORY EXPERIMENTS

For experiment in the ecostat chambers, buds of *Convolvulus sepium* were used. Figure 34 shows the percentage opening of a typical set under constant conditions of 15°, 20°, and 30°, darkness, and 25 per cent relative humidity.

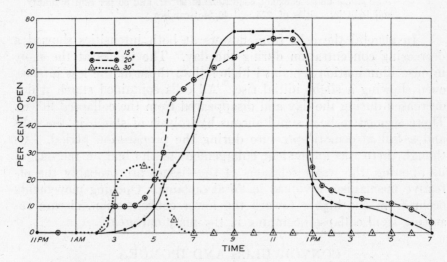

Fig. 34.—Percentage opening of flowers of *Convolvulus sepium* under constant conditions of darkness and 25 per cent relative humidity, and 15°, 20°, and 30° C.

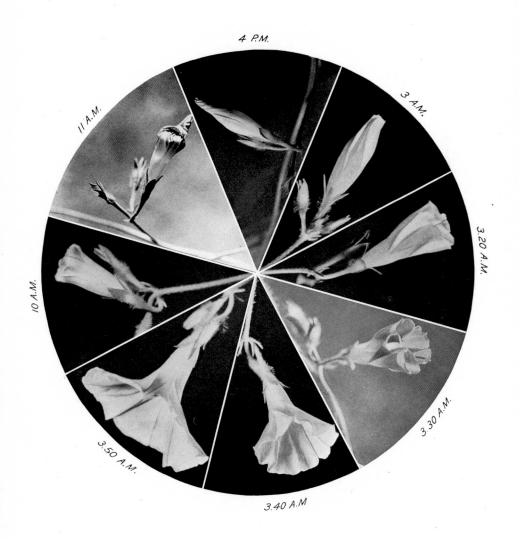

Flower cycle of *Ipomoea purpurea*

It will be seen that under these conditions the degree of expansion was inversely proportional to the temperature, being greatest at 15° and least at 30°. The time of the beginning of the opening movement was earlier at the higher temperatures, but the rates of opening varied irregularly, being 12, 6, and 7, at 15°, 20°, and 30° respectively. When a humidity of 70 per cent was maintained in the experimental chambers, similar experiments the details of which are omitted, gave opposite results, the average maximum openings being 10, 27, 52, 85, and 86, for temperatures of 12°, 15°, 20°, 25°, and 30° respectively. That a humidity of 25 per cent became a limiting factor at the higher temperatures is not surprising, for the water supply present in the bud is utilized in opening. This is shown by the fact that buds severed from the parent stem at 10 P.M. opened at the usual time in the morning when exposed in the field without a water supply. The sudden changes in temperature occurring at the time of the transfer of the flowers from the field or from storage to the ecostat chambers did not result in an immediate movement, this appearing only at or near the periodic time for such a reaction. The transpiration from the flowers of *Convolvulus* during the night was very low.

TISSUE STUDIES

Studies by the plasmolytic method showed that the osmotic concentrations in the cells of the outer and inner epidermis of *Convolvulus* followed a curve somewhat similar to that of *Mirabilis*. In *Convolvulus arvensis* both the outer and inner epidermis of the bud gave a value equal to .7 molar sucrose solution. In the field the values became .6 for the outer epidermis and 1 for the inner at the beginning of opening, and dropped to .5 on both surfaces in the closed flower.

TRADESCANTIA VIRGINIANA

Stages in the opening of the flowers of *Tradescantia virginiana* are shown in Plate 29. The mature buds which have been directed downward during the immature period assume the erect position on the day preceding that of opening, enlargement of the corolla occurring simultaneously. The calyx lobes begin to separate at 7 to 9 P.M., and slowly open, while the corolla unrolls and spreads to full expansion by 5 A.M. Usually the corolla withers and the tips fold in by midforenoon, but the flowers may remain fresh during cool moist days. As the petals collapse, the sepals close and the old flower is directed downward into the position of the bud, leaving the developing ovary protected by the calyx, and the inflorescence clear, ready for the display of the next flowers.

Open flowers enclosed in a moistened bell jar remained open throughout the day, while adjacent ones closed by 10 A.M. The same result was achieved by lowering the temperature to 15°, and indicates that temperature is at least partly effective through its influence on the transpiration rate. Cut flowers supplied with water and exposed in the habitat behaved similarly to those growing on the plant.

Cut flowers placed in the experimental chambers at 12 midnight, under constant conditions of darkness and 50 per cent humidity, remained closed until noon at 10°, opened to 30 per cent at 3 A.M. at 15°, to 55 per cent at 3:30 A.M. at 20°, and to full expansion at 4 A.M. at 25°. The flowers evidently reached a degree of maximum expansion directly proportional to the temperature.

Plasmolytic studies showed that the osmotic concentration of the epidermal cells in the unopened bud was equal on the two surfaces with a value of .30 molar. The values for the outer and inner surfaces respectively were .35 and .50 during opening, and decreased to .30 and .35 just before collapse.

Mature buds expanded to a limited degree when placed in water, and longitudinal sections made during the early part of the night opened in 30 minutes and closed again when transfered to .2M sucrose solution. Both the calyx and corolla were active, and the final angle attained in water or sucrose solutions varied with the osmotic concentration.

LINUM

The flowers of *Linum perenne, L. angustifolium,* and *L. usitatissimum* are similar in behavior, opening during the night or early morning, the petals falling before noon. Opening requires about 1 hour. The calyx spreads slowly, and after the fall of the corolla closes over the developing fruit. The time both of opening and of closing is variable. The flowers may be kept open throughout the day by enclosing them in a moistened bell jar or cooling to 10° to 15°. In the field the flowers first exposed to light open before those in shade. When enclosed in a bell jar heated to 25° at 60 per cent humidity, the flowers opened at once when the heat was applied between 1 and 3 A.M., but did not respond when this treatment was applied before midnight.

LABORATORY EXPERIMENTS

The percentage opening of the flowers of *L. usitatissimum* under constant conditions of darkness, 10 per cent relative humidity, and 10°, 20°, and 30° is given in Table 34. These flowers were removed from the field at 6 P.M. and stored at 8°, darkness, and 100 per cent humidity, until placed in the experimental chambers.

Flower cycle of *Tradescantia virginiana*

Periodic opening appeared under all conditions tried, expansion beginning in the early morning. The periodic nature of the response is also shown by the fact that the sudden change from the conditions

TABLE 34

LINUM USITATISSIMUM

Behavior (per cent open) of flowers under constant conditions of darkness, 10% humidity, and 10°, 20°, and 30° C.

w. flowers wilting.

Temp. °C.	10	10	10	20	20	20	30	30	30
Time									
7 p.m.	0			0			0		
8	0			0			0		
9	0			0			0		
10	0			0			0		
11	0			0			0		
12 mt.	0	0		0	0		0	0	
1 a.m.	0	0		0	0		0	0	
2	0	0		0	0		0	10	
3	0	10	5	1	25	25	10	10	25
4	0	10	5	2	30	25	10	10	25
5	6	10	7	12	40	25	15	10	20
6	7	10	10	50	60	25	100	10	10
7	8	10	10	55	63	25	100	10	10
8	10	10	10	63	68	35	100	10	10
9	10	10	10	65	75	40	100	w	w
10	10	10	10	67	82	40	100	w	w
11	0	10	10	50	90	40	w	w	w
12 m.	0	10	10	38	90	40	w	w	w
1 p.m.	0	10	10	25	80	35	w	w	w

of storage to those of the ecostat chambers resulted in an immediate response only at 3 A.M. At 30° the low humidity became critical and wilting followed. Oddly enough, the flowers given the maximum exposure reached the full open condition. When the temperature change was made at 3 A.M. while opening was under way, closing followed.

At 20° the flowers opened to an average maximum of 78 per cent for the first two series removed from storage before opening was under way. But little movement occurred at 10°, the maximum opening being 10 per cent. The series in which the opening movements were not in progress at the time of transfer, and in which the maximum opening was reached before wilting, showed maximum expansions of 10, 78, and 100, and opening rates of 6, 9, and 25, at 10°, 20°, and 30° respectively, both the degree and the rate of expansion varying directly with the temperature.

X

DISCUSSION

FIELD BEHAVIOR

The field behavior of flowers, though constant in its general aspects, shows variability when given close inspection. Thus the flowers of *Tulipa gesneriana* open regularly in the morning and close at night, but sometimes depart from this behavior. On cool days the flowers may remain closed, while during hot and windy periods closure occurs during the forenoon. Heads of *Taraxacum officinale* commonly open in the morning, the time depending on the advance of the season and hence the temperature, and close either at evening or during the day. With the varying intensity of habitat factors, opening may occur from 5 to 10 A.M., and closure from 9 A.M. to 6 P.M. Limited parts of the habitat with less intense desiccating conditions due to shade or protection from the wind may exhibit striking differences in the time of movement of the heads occurring there. Many flowers, such as those of *Tragopogon* and *Mentzelia*, show similar sensitivity to habitat conditions; they may open at different times of day, and reopen for a varying number of sucessive periods. Both the time of reaction and the longevity of these flowers varies with the habitat, the flowers growing in protected locations or at higher altitudes behaving later in the season as do those in warmer habitats earlier in the season.

The length of the period during which floral movements occur varies even more than the floral behavior. *Acroclinium roseum* commonly remains active in some degree for nearly a month, *Layia elegans* for several weeks, *Aster bigelovi* for one to two weeks, *Taraxacum, Crepis,* and *Tragopogon* for two days to a week, and *Linum rubrum* and *Tribulus terrestris* for one to two days, depending on the conditions which promote rapid desiccation. Thus in the hemeranthous group, flowers display various degrees of persistence and may become ephemeral under the more severe field conditions. Flowers of the ephemeral hemeranthous group show similar variability, differing only in the degree of resistance to the evaporational conditions of the habitat. The various species of *Convolvulus* and of *Ipomoea* usually collapse in the forenoon, but remain open throughout the day when low evaporational conditions obtain. *Ipomoea rubro-coerulea* is more resistant to day conditions and remains open till noon or later on most summer days. The petals of *Erodium* fall

182

while in an apparently fresh condition, the flowers of *Tradescantia* wither during collapse, and the flowers of *Hibiscus trionum* close while still turgid. The flowers of *Portulaca* remain open throughout the day if the temperature is not excessive, but do not reopen; this is also the behavior of *Tribulus* during the driest conditions of late summer. Evidently the closing movements may occur at any time when the rate of floral transpiration exceeds that of water conduction to the tissues concerned. This condition may occur early or late in the day. A loss in tissue turgidity results in closure, dropping of floral organs, or withering and collapse.

The characteristic common to the various hemeranthous flowers is the time of opening. Nyctanthous and ephemeral nyctanthous flowers both open shortly after dusk. The *Mentzelias* and *Silene noctiflora* repeat their movements on several successive nights. While the flowers of *Silene* remain open throughout the night, those of the *Mentzelias* have a period of expansion of but a few hours. The flowers of the *Oenotheras* enlarge and develop during the day a tissue tension in the sepals sufficient to bulge these structures outward and finally tear them apart. This separation allows the release of the petals which are also under a tension built up during the daylight period. The conditions of this preparation period during which the tissue tension develops are sufficiently severe to cause the collapse of the expanded petals on the following day when the cells are senescent. The time of opening of such flowers evidently depends on the completion of the preparation for opening rather than on the conditions obtaining at the time expansion actually occurs. It is not to be expected that the modification of factors in the field will greatly alter floral movements, unless they are of a critical intensity such that all movements are checked or the tissues injured, or unless they are prolonged over a considerable portion of the preparation period for opening.

Temperature, light, and humidity can be modified to some degree by a simple apparatus suitable for field use, but the regulation of these factors is subject to considerable variation and it is not practicable to prolong such experiments over one or more preparation periods. The results in the present study show in many cases merely a modification of the speed of movements already under way, or the prolongation of the open period by the reduction in the intensity of the evaporation conditions. The flowers of *Tulipa* and of the species of *Gentiana* studied were exceptions in responding directly in some degree to the temperatures applied, as were those of *Acroclinium roseum* in responding to humidity levels. It was found possible to hasten the opening of many different species of flowers by increasing the temperature, and to retard it by the reverse change. As a consequence of high humidity and the absence of wind in the laboratory, flowers could be kept open for a much longer period than was usual in the field. Opening processes could seldom be initiated in the field except at a time when preparation for opening was complete and the daily periodic opening could be considered in progress even though not yet detectable by observation.

As has been frequently recorded by other workers, the flowers of *Tulipa* can be induced to carry out opening and closing movements by suitable temperature changes. It may be that here we are dealing with a differential tissue reaction a part of which is directly attributable to the living protoplasm, as Bünning suggests, but it seems rather a matter of the water relations of the tissues. This is indicated by the movements of the perianth parts when placed in solutions of different concentrations, as was described by Farmer and confirmed in the present study. It does not seem probable that in such cases growth can be concerned, except in the limited phase which depends on the stretching of the cells by the pressure of their contents. The lack of contraction on the concave surface which has been accepted since the researches of Pfeffer merely shows the lack of elasticity in the tissue and not any essential difference in mechanism from that here assumed.

It is difficult to conceive of a condition in which the expansion of the flower would not affect the rate of transpiration, but no such influence could be detected by the methods here employed. This may have been due to the inaccuracies unavoidable in a method which requires periodic weighings and a comparison with evaporation from a free-water surface. The results show a general parallel between the floral transpiration and the evaporation and indicate only cuticular transpiration. This is confirmed by observation of the stomata which are usually closed and probably functionless. The longitudinal rolling of the petals which occurs under extreme desiccating conditions in the older flowers of *Tulipa, Eschscholtzia, Tribulus,* and *Silene* is apparently a response to high transpiration, but no results of the present study bear on this point.

The fact that cutting rarely produces any noticeable change in floral behavior for 24 hours or more, and that flowers cut immediately before opening and left exposed in the field without a water supply frequently opened at the usual time, shows that a water supply from the parent plant is not of immediate necessity at the time of opening. Studies of the water content of the flowers indicated a general decrease with age, but no change which could be directly correlated with the movements except in a few species. It seems probable that although water content is commonly high at the time of opening, the exchange of water to which the movements are due is rather between tissues than between organs of the flower or other parts of the plant, with the important exception of *Hibiscus trionum*.

The water content of a tissue, and hence its turgidity, will vary with osmotic concentration, hydration of the colloids, permeability of the membrane, and the conditions of water loss and supply. In a cut flower which opens with the water supply contained in its own tissues the turgidity of the cells concerned in floral movements will be proportional to the osmotic concentration, the hydration of the protoplasm and the equilibrium relations between these and the evap-orational conditions. For tissues concerned in floral movements the environment will comprise the adjacent tissues and the external factors under which the flower expands. Any change in these can be expected to produce changes in turgidity. It is not difficult to see the possible relations of temperature and light, and to recognize that in so complicated a balance a simple relation between movement and any single factor cannot be expected. It is also evi-dent that the conditions under which a given turgidity relation de-velops are at least as important as those obtaining at the time of the visible part of the reaction. That is, a reaction such as the opening of a flower is predetermined by the conditions present before the visible movement takes place. Such an explanation tends to remove the mystery of autonomic reactions and leaves the conditions of the preparation period capable of experimental study and exact de-termination.

LABORATORY EXPERIMENTS

Working under the comparatively exact conditions of the labora-tory makes more detailed studies possible. Even here the conditions must be subjected to constant scrutiny, for a small variation which in comparison to the changes observed in the field seems insignificant, may be decisive. Bünning found that variations of one degree or less are significant in the behavior of the flowers of *Tulipa*. Equivalent variations in other factors cannot be safely discounted and it is probable that the wide differences in the results of much of the work reported are due to the neglect of the accurate control of one or more factors. Such errors were reduced as far as possible in the present work by a carefully adjusted automatic control supplemented by constant inspection over considerable periods.

Under constant conditions such as were employed in the present study, flowers generally show periodic opening and closing movements during the first 24 hours after removal from the field. That is, the general features of the daily behavior of these flowers were predetermined for at least one day after removal from the field and subjection to constant conditions. All expression of this periodicity could usually be checked by temperatures of 10° and 35°, but in many cases prolonged exposure to these temperatures did not prevent the reappearance of the movements when more favorable temperature levels were reestablished. Flowers of species well adapted to different ecological habitats, such as the various altitudes, often behaved differently at low temperatures.

The strength of periodicity, as measured by the deegree of maximum expansion and rate of movement under constant conditions and in response to temperature changes, differs greatly in the different forms. In the flowers of *Taraxacum* and similar forms, periodicity is strong and modifies all floral movements, even after the flowers have been kept under constant conditions for several days. In the flowers of *Tulipa,* periodicity is weak and can easily be overlooked since stimuli of moderate intensity entirely mask it. Under constant conditions it is conspicuous but remains effective for only a single day. The gentians also show a weak periodicity, and in the studies here made none was observed in *G. calycosa* and *G. frigida.* It is probable that a more detailed study would show its presence. In *Acroclinium* no periodicity exists, a given stimulus producing the same response at any period during the day. In this case we are dealing with a physical process taking place in the cell walls. Periodicity is evidently connected with living cells and indicates that at least in this important regard they are directly concerned in flower movements.

Although most flowers exhibit periodic expansion under the constant conditions of the experimental chambers, this opening shows great variability in extent but not in time. In the field these responses are reenforced by the changing factors of the habitat, the result being the full degrees of floral movement. Under experimental conditions these movements can be distinguished and their relative importance determined for each species. That is, the strength of periodicity in any flower may be measured by the degree and rate of opening under constant conditions. Thus periodic opening and closing progresses to completion in the flowers of most Compositae, but in *Tulipa* results in but partial opening at temperatures which will not mask the effect.

The persistence of the daily periodic movements also varies with different species and with the conditions under which the flowers are kept. In general, low temperatures are more favorable to the persistence of periodic movements than are high ones. Light acts in a similar manner, though with important exceptions. The flowers of *Taraxacum* show periodic movements which persist to the second day only at temperatures below 25°, while those of *Eschscholtzia* show no periodic movements after 24 hours at 10°, darkness, and 100 per cent humidity.

The factors that establish the daily rhythm probably differ among species and in various habitats in which these factors may approach the limiting level. This predetermining period has not received in the past the consideration it merits. It is the effect of the factors during this preparation period which controls many of the floral movements, and this influence may persist for a considerable duration of time. Stoppel and others have shown that a change in the daily period of temperature or illumination may produce other periodic responses related in time to the artificially established rhythm. The results of the present study show that in all hemeranthous forms in which periodic movements are apparent, temperatures of 10° and 15° are followed by a greater rate and amplitude of movement than occur when the flowers are kept at a higher level. At temperatures of 30° or more, periodic movements in most species disappear in 24 hours. Light has an effect similar to that of temperature. Humidity seems to be without influence in most forms, but is of striking importance in *Tragopogon*.

The duration of exposure and the period of the day in which this occurs is of great importance to the periodic behavior of flowers. Thus exposure in the field during the forenoon results in a greater rate and amplitude of movement in the flowers of *Tulipa* than does a similar period of exposure during the afternoon. Similarly, the maximum movement of the flowers of *Taraxacum* and of *Aster bigelovi* is favored by exposure to afternoon and night conditions up to midnight, and those of *Crepis* up to 9 A.M. In nyctanthous flowers a similar rule holds, except that the critical conditions of the preparation period are those of daylight. Thus the activity of the flowers of *Mentzelia multiflora* is greatest when they have been exposed to daylight conditions for a period of 9 to 12 hours immediately preceding the time of opening. In other words, the opening of these flowers takes place in the normal manner and to the greatest degree when the preparation period has been passed under conditions similar to those commonly obtaining in the field; that is, low temperatures and darkness for hemeranthous forms, and high temperatures and light intensities for nyctanthous. Since cut flowers exhibit the same behavior, connection with the plant is not a factor of importance during the limited time used in the experimentation for these studies.

The behavior of cut flowers after storage under constant conditions shows a similar relation. Flowers of *Tulipa, Taraxacum,* and many other Compositae showed the maximum rate and degree of opening after storage at 10°, darkness, and 100% humidity during the night period to 6 A.M., but this treatment had the opposite effect when continued through the daylight period. Flowers of *Eschscholtzia* subjected to sudden temperature changes between 15° and 30° after storage under conditions similar to those just mentioned for 3, 6, 11, and 16 hours, opened in direct proportion to the hours of storage. The opening of the flowers of *Mentzelia nuda* was favored by storage during the night at 15° and darkness, but was reduced in extent and rate if this storage was prolonged into the daylight period. Similarly, *M. multiflora* gave a greater degree of opening after storage during the night at 10°, darkness, and 100% humidity; but when this storage occurred during daylight, not only the rate and degree of movement was reduced but the time of these movements was also displaced in varying degrees, this treatment disturbing the periodic rhythm predetermined on the previous day. When such treatment was continued for periods up to 153 hours, floral movements were affected in proportion to the number of daylight storage hours immediately preceding opening. The storage of cut *Mentzelia* flowers at 20°, 40 foot-candles light intensity, and 50 per cent humidity resulted in floral behavior similar to that following daylight storage conditions.

It is evident that periodic movements in flowers are determined in large degree by the complex of factors in the field during the period immediately preceding floral opening, and that this predetermination is more or less persistent in the different species. In general this preparation is favored by low temperatures and darkness for hemeranthous species, and by moderately high temperatures and light for the nyctanthous. Since connection with the plant is not necessary, preparation is to be regarded as an inter-tissue balance of water relations and tensions. The importance of the humidity-periodic relations of *Tragopogon* flowers points to the intimate connection between these and the factors in the field.

TEMPERATURE RELATIONS

From the preceding discussion it is evident that factor effects must be considered both in their relation to the preparation period for opening, and to the flower at the time movements are taking place. Some details of the former relation have already been discussed. Of the temperatures used for hemeranthous forms, the lower favored the preparation for opening, and the higher checked or prevented this movement, depending on the length of treatment and the time of the day during which it was applied. The nyctanthous forms require a higher temperature and also illumination during the daylight period immediately before opening. Temperature conditions of the preparation period affect the degree and rate of movement, but if the time of application is varied the entire periodic relation may be displaced. Preparation for opening goes on at 10° or 15°, even though the opening of the flower cannot actually occur at this temperature. The preparation for opening both of hemeranthous and nyctanthous flowers is favored by low night temperatures, but the latter are also favored by high day temperatures. The effects of temperature during the preparation period are not cumulative beyond the day immediately preceding opening. It is obvious that the practice of florists in placing cut flowers in refrigeration for a short time before marketing depends in part for its efficacy on this favorable effect of low temperature storage.

Minimal, optimal, and maximal temperatures were not specially determined in this study, but few species showed appreciable movement at 10° or at 30° and above. It is of interest to note that even here lines cannot be definitely drawn, but that movement is the expression of a critical balance of conditions which may be greatly altered by an apparently minute and insignificant change. Thus 15° checks all movement in the flowers of *Mentzelia nuda* during the first day after storage at 12° and darkness till 2 P.M., but favors the opening process after 24 hours under these conditions. In dealing with the movements of flowers we must recognize the complicated and critical balance of factors which gives not the simple time-temperature relation frequently assumed, but a time-temperature-periodicity relation in which the effects of a condition may be expressed either in the preparation for opening or directly in the movement. The effects of this preparation may modify the rate and extent of the temperature response or, as in *Taraxacum*, even reverse its direction.

The temperatures obtaining when the opening process is under way are much more simply related to floral movement than are those in effect during the preparation period. In a few flowers such as those of *Tulipa* and *Gentiana* the periodic relations are masked by the effects of temperature so that the relations appear direct, as indeed they are. The difference between this behavior and the more complicated behavior of such species as *Taraxacum* is one of degree rather than of kind. In all flowers examined in the present study, the relation between rate and degree of opening and the temperature at the time of this movement is direct within the critical limits of 10° to 25° or 30°, unless humidity or light is at the level of a limiting factor. Comparisons can only be made at the equilibrium positions, and between flowers which have had similar treatment during the preparation periods. This direct relation between the temperature and the degree of opening shows an adjustment to the conditions of the habitat in which the plant occurs, the temperature levels producing a given response being low in plants from cooler habitats.

Sudden temperature changes produce in most flowers a different response from that caused by a constant temperature similar to the one to which the change was made. Such temperature changes are effective in many species in causing conspicuous movements if they parallel the direction of periodicity; but result in slight response, or none, or less frequently in a reverse reaction, if they oppose it. Such response is probably connected directly with the living protoplasm and is to be regarded as evidence of irritability. The amplitude of this movement is small and it plays but a minor part in floral activity. It doubtless accounts for the slight closing movement frequently following cutting, and for the occasional reversal of reaction accompanying a sudden temperature change.

Heretofore it has been believed that the time between the application of a stimulus and the reaction was a latent period in which several things occurred which were not well understood. It is brought out by the work discussed in this book that this latent period depends for its length not only on the stimulus and its intensity but on predetermined periodicity. In all autonomic movement it is very probable that periodicity and predetermination play a large part.

EFFECTS OF LIGHT

As in the case of temperature, the action of light on floral movements must be considered in its effect both during the preparation period and directly on the movement itself. The fact that the most favorable preparation period in hemeranthous forms is during darkness, points to the unfavorableness of light for the predetermination of movement. The degree of expansion of the flowers of *Eschscholtzia* is appreciably reduced by exposure to 40 foot-candles light intensity during part of the preparation period. The periodic movements of *Tulipa* are largely conditioned by the factors during the forenoon. The flowers of *Mentzelia nuda* showed a direct relation between the degree of expansion and the temperature only when the storage period at 10° and darkness did not exceed four hours of the daylight period. It seems probable that in the establishment of the critical balance of the preparation period light is a factor of great importance.

The direct effect of light on floral movements appears in a number of cases and is probably quite general if it can be disentangled from the effects of periodicity and temperature. The flowers of *Tulipa* and *Hibiscus* show a direct relation between the degree of expansion and the light intensity. Similar relations were displayed by *Mentzelia nuda*, which also showed acceleration in the rate of opening. In contrast to this the flowers of *Eschscholtzia* and of *Mirabilis* opened to a reduced maximum under constant light intensity of 40 foot-candles. The time at which the maximum was reached was earlier in the two forms just mentioned and in *Arctotis*, but the opening movements of *Taraxacum* and of *Aster bigelovi* were retarded by light. It is probable that a study of light intensity-time relations would explain most of these apparent differences.

Sudden changes in light intensity produce effects comparable to those due to changes in temperature, but at the intensities used in the present study, the maximum of which was 40 foot-candles, this stimulatory action was less pronounced. The flowers of *Tulipa* opened in response to a sudden change from darkness to 40 foot-candles light intensity, and closed slightly in response to a reversal in light conditions. *Taraxacum* and like Compositae displayed a similar reaction, but the movements were evident only when the direction of the stimulus paralleled that of periodicity. It is only in this limited sense that an influence of light on the rays of *Tragopogon*, suggested by Palladin and Livingston, can be true.

EFFECTS OF HUMIDITY

No habitat factor has received less consideration than atmospheric humidity, yet from this limited basis most workers in the field of flower movement agree in according it little importance. More work is needed on this subject, with the recognition that plant response is the result of the total complex of factors in which one or more of the constituents may play the conspicuous part and yet be effective only in the presence of the others. In such a complex the relative importance of any factor varies not only with its intensity but also with that of the others, and becomes conspicuous when critical limiting conditions are approached.

The present study shows that, measured by floral activity, humidity at times plays an important part and is effective within the range of ordinary field conditions in a number of species. The maximum degree of expansion of the flowers of *Tulipa* is reduced by exposure to 90 per cent humidity. The flowers of *Taraxacum* and of *Eschscholtzia* show a similar but more marked depression of the degree of opening, and also a prolongation of the open period. For flowers of *Convolvulus sepium* humidity of 25 per cent is limiting, so that the reactions to other factors, such as temperature, are altered and the relations confused. The periodicity of the flowers of *Tragopogon* is closely related to the humidity conditions, at least in cut flowers. The periodic opening following the cutting of closed heads is checked at low humidities. In this case there is a distinctly limiting critical humidity relation for the preparation period. The flowers of *Acro-clinium roseum* respond to the humidity of the atmosphere in which the heads occur, closing at a high value and opening when this falls to a lower level. Movement in these flowers is apparently the result of differential expansion due to the hygroscopicity of opposed tissue layers. In this flower there is little evidence of the activity of the living cells, the curvature being due to the differential swelling of the materials of which the walls are composed. This behavior, though not found in other flowers, seems common to those with scarious bracts similar to those of *Acroclinium*.

MECHANISM

Although all floral organs may show movement during their life-history, only the bracts, sepals, and petals have been considered in the present study. In these organs the greater part of the curvature which results in floral movement occurs in a very limited region near the base of the organ concerned. Since the organs in the bud are usually convex they do not readily allow the curvature necessary for opening, so that an inconspicuous and early stage of the opening movement is a flattening in the basal region. This is the antithesis of the longitudinal rolling of the petals of *Eschscholtzia* and of *Tribulus* when the older flowers close under severe evaporational conditions. In tubular corollas unfolding sometimes occurs, but more commonly only the lobes are reflexed, the basal region exhibiting the most active curvature.

The structure of the active region varies greatly in different species, and in different organs of the same species. In *Tulipa* this region is composed of a considerable mass of parenchymatous tissue arranged, as Farmer has shown, so as to permit movement without shearing. Intercellular spaces are conspicuous. The flowers of *Eschscholtzia, Calochortus,* and *Rosa* have a more or less thickened region of curvature in the corolla. Most flowers display this characteristic in the bracts and sepals, which are chlorophyll bearing and frequently show active opening and closing movements. In organs of this sort it is probable that the changes in the water relations of the tissues occur within the structure, but it is obvious that such changes to be effective must be on opposite sides of a region in which little change in size takes place.

In many flowers, such as those of the Compositae, the corolla is composed of loose spongy tissue supporting the epidermal layers. In such a structure the epidermis is most favorably located for producing curvature and is to be regarded as the most active tissue in such movements. The epidermis is also most directly influenced by the changing factors of the habitat, and is affected both by the atmospheric conditions and by those of the tissues beneath the surface. This layer is thus important in floral movement, directly in those organs which consist of spongy parenchyma, and indirectly in those in which the mass of cells beneath are also active.

Many flowers can be caused to exhibit opening and closing movements by the treatment either of the entire flower or of the longitudinal section with water or with solutions of sucrose of various concentrations. Most movements of this sort can be produced repeatedly, except in ephemeral forms where closure is collapse. It is obvious that these movements are due to a disturbance of the water relations of the tissues, but there is no proof that they are essentially the same under laboratory treatment as those occurring in the field. Since the positions attained are equilibrium angles, the movements are not due to rate of water movement within the tissues. The ligules of *Taraxacum* and similar Compositae exhibit an opening movement when placed in water, and a closing movement in sucrose solutions of .1 molar or stronger, the process requiring 1 to 2 hours. The flowers of *Tulipa* respond oppositely, opening in molar sucrose solution, and closing in water. Since these flowers are hemeranthous, the difference shows a relation to the permeability of the external cuticularized surface, rather than to the internal tissues, as would be the case when natural movements were in progress. The direction of the movements taking place in water or in sucrose solutions can be varied at will in the bracts of *Tragopogon* by scraping away the cuticle from the outer or inner surface, the movements then being away from the scraped surface in water, and toward it in molar sucrose solution. Tissue tension studies in flower parts show that artificial alterations of the tissues through the epidermis can produce the movements observed in nature. These are probably activated by similar alterations brought about through internal adjustments.

The osmotic concentrations of the epidermal cells stripped from opposite surfaces of the regions showing the greatest curvature was determined by the plasmolytic method at various times during floral activity. These studies showed in many species a falling value with age, and a daily periodic fluctuation. In this rhythm the values were greater on the inner surface than on the outer during the preparation period. This relation approached equality on the two surfaces during opening and assumed a reversed relation before closing, the outer epidermal layer showing a higher osmotic concentration than the inner. The difference reached a maximum of .2 molar in many species, and commonly appeared shortly before the movements which followed from the stronger toward the weaker side. These relations appeared quite general in flowers in which the floral organs were thin and the epidermal layers represented a considerable portion of the tissue. In the more massive organs the relations still appeared but were more variable.

Differences in osmotic concentration between the opposite surfaces may not directly cause the flower movements, but when such movements occur they progress from the stronger toward the weaker side and pass through a period of equal concentration on both surfaces to a reverse relation and a movement in the reverse direction. It seems probable that the water relations of the tissues are profoundly modified by the daily cycle of concentration in the tissues. The result of the adjustments is the movement of the part concerned. The intimate relation between the concentrations and the floral movements is also indicated by the fact that ephemeral flowers pass through only the first portion of the concentration cycle followed by hemeranthous and nyctanthous forms, the outer epidermis of the ephemeral forms never reaching the higher concentration which precedes closing movements. In such forms closing is collapse of the corolla.

BIBLIOGRAPHY

ANDREWS, F. M. 1929. The effect of temperature on flowers. Plant Phys. 4:281–284.

ATKINS, W. R. G. 1916. Some recent researches in plant physiology.

BALFOUR, J. 1875. Manual of botany.

BALL, N. B. 1926. Transmission of stimuli in plants. Nature 118:589–590.

BECK, W. A. 1927. Cane sugar and potassium nitrate as plasmolyzing agents. Protoplasma. 1:15–72.

———. 1929. Determining the osmotic value at incipient plasmolysis. Trans. Am. Mic. Soc. 48:204–208.

BENECKE, W. and JOST, L. 1924. Pflanzenphysiologie.

BLACKMANN, F. F. and PAINE, S. G. 1918. Permeability in Mimosa pulvini. Ann. Bot. 32:69–85.

BOSE, J. C. 1916. Plant response.

——— and PRASSANNA, G. 1925. Physiological and anatomical investigations on Mimosa pudica. Proc. Roy. Soc. 98:290–312.

BRAUNER, L. 1922. Lichtkrümmung und Lichtwachstumsreaktion. Zeit. Bot. 14:497–547.

———. 1924. Permeabilität und Phototropismus. Zeit. Bot. 16:113–132.

———. 1926. Über den Einfluss der Temperatur auf die phototropische Variationsbewegungen von Phaseolus multiflorus, Ein Erwiderung auf H. Gradmanns Einwände. Jahrb. Wiss. Bot. 65:639–642.

BROWN, WM. H. and TRELEASE, S. F. 1918. Alternate shrinkage and elongation of growing stems of Cestrum nocturnum. Phil. Jour. Sci. 13:352–360.

BÜNNING, E. 1929. Über die Thermonastischen und Thigmonastischen Blütenbewegungen. Planta. 8:698–716.

BURGERSTEIN, A. 1902. Über die Bewegungerscheinungen der Perigonblätter von Tulipa und Crocus. (Jahresbericht des k. k. Erzherzog Rainer-Gymnasiums in Wien 1902). Bot. Centralbl. 90:665.

———. 1902. Über die Verteilung der Spaltöffnungen in Beziehung zur Schlafstellung.

CONRAD, H. S. 1903. How a water lily opens. Country Life Am. 4:312–313.

COWDRY, E. V. 1924. General cytology.

CROZIER, W. J. 1926–1927. On curves of growth especially in relation to temperature. Jour. Gen. Phys. 10:53–73.

DARWIN, C. and DARWIN, F. 1880. The power of movement in plants.

DARWIN, F. and PERTZ, D. F. M. 1903. On the artificial production of rhythm in plants. Ann. Bot. 17:93–106.

DAVY DE VIRVILLE, A. and OBATON, F. 1922. Observations et expériences sur les fleurs éphémères. Compt. Rend. Acad. Sci. Paris. 175:637–640.

———. 1923. Étude biologique de l'expanoussement des fleurs. Rev. Gén. Bot. 35:161–185.

DE CANDOLLE, A. P. 1835. Physiologie végétal.

DE SAUSSURE, M. T. 1822. De l'action de fleurs sur l'air, et de leur chaleur propre. Ann. Chem. Phys. 21:279–303.

DE VRIES, H. 1877. Untersuchungen über die mechanischen Ursachen des Zellstrechung ausgehend von der Einwirkung von Salzlösungen auf der Turgor wachsender Pflanzenzellen.

———. 1884. Eine Methode zur Analyse der Turgorkraft. Jahrb. Wiss. Bot. 14:427–601.

DIXON, H. H. 1914. Transpiration and the ascent of sap in plants.

DOWLING, J. J. 1923. The recording ultramicrometer, its principles and application. Phil. Mag. 46:81–100.

DUTROCHET, M. 1836. Reveille et sommeil des fleurs. Ann. Sci. Nat. Bot. 2:6:177–189.

ERBAN, M. 1916. Über die Verteilung der Spaltöffnungen in Beziehung zur Schlafstellung der Blätter. Ber. Deut. Bot. Ges. 34:880–890.

FARMER, J. B. 1902. On the mechanism which is concerned in effecting the opening and closing of tulip flowers. New Phyt. 1:56–58.

FITTING, H. 1903. Untersuchungen über der Haptotropismus der Ranken. Jahrb. Wiss. Bot. 38:545–632.

———. 1902. Untersuchungen über der Haptotropismus der Ranken. Ber. Deut. Bot. Ges. 20:373–382.

GARDNER, W. 1887. On the power of contractility exhibited by the protoplasm of certain plant cells. Ann. Bot. 1:362–367.

GOEBEL, K. 1920. Die Entfaltungsbewegungen der Pflanzen und deren teleologische Deutung.

GUTTENBERG, H. 1925. Die Bewegungsmechanik des Laubblättes von Dionaea muscipula Ell. Flora 118–119:165–183. Bot. Abs. 15:n. 3728. 1926.

HABERLANDT, G. 1914. Physiological plant anatomy. Trans. by Montagu Drummond.

HANSGIRG, A. 1890. Ueber die Verbreitung der karpotropischen Nutationskrümmungen der Kelch-, Hull- und ähnlicher Blätter und der Blüthenstiele. Ber. Deut. Bot. Ges. 8:345–355.

———. 1890. Beiträge zur Kenntnis über die Verbreitung der Reizbewegungen und der nyctitropischen Variations-bewegungen der Laubblätter. Ber. Deut. Bot. Ges. 8:355–364.

———. 1896. Neue Untersuchungen über den Gamo- und Karpotropismus sowie über die Reiz- und Schlafbewegungen der Blüthen und Laubblätter. Königl. Böhm. Ges. Wiss.

———. 1904. Pflanzenbiologische Untersuchungen.

HARRIS, J. A., LAWRENCE, J. V. and GORTNER, R. A. 1916. The cryoscopic constants of expressed vegetable sap as related to local conditions in the Arizona desert. Phys. Res. 2:1–49.

———. 1917. The relation between the osmotic concentration of leaf sap and the height of leaf insertion in trees. Bull. Torr. Bot. Club. 44:267–286.

HENDRICKS, H. V. 1919. Torsion studies in twining plants. Bot. Gaz. 68:425–440.

———. 1923. Torsion studies in twining plants II. Bot. Gaz. 75:282–297.

HENSEL, E. P. 1905. On the movement of petals. Univ. Neb. Studies. 5:191–228.

HOEBER, R. 1914. Physiologische Chemie der Zelle und der Gewebe.

HOFFMAN, H. 1850. Recherches sur le sommeil des plantes. Ann. Sci. Nat. Bot. 3:14:310–330.

HÖFLER, K. 1928. Über Kappenplasmolysis. Ber. Deut. Bot. Ges. 46:73–82.

HOFMEISTER, W. 1868. Allgemeine Morphologie der Gewächse.

HOTTES, H. F., and HAFENRICHTER, A. L. 1928. A constant rate aspirator. Science. 67:320–322.

ILJIN, W. S. 1914. Die Regulierung der Spaltöffnungen mit der Veränderung des osmotischen Drucks. Beih. Bot. Centralbl. 32:15–36.

IVANOW, S. 1927. Zur Physiologie der Korolle. Ber. Deut. Bot. Ges. 45:582–587.

JOST, L. 1895. Ueber die Abhängigkeit des Laubblättes von seiner Assimilationstatigkeit. Jahrb. Wiss. Bot. 27:403–480.

———. 1898. Beiträge zur Kenntnis der nyctitropischen Bewegungen. Jahrb. Wiss. Bot. 31:345–390.

———. 1902. Botanischen Jahresbericht. 30:612–613.

———. 1904. Vorlesungen über Pflanzenphysiologie.

KABSCH, W. 1862. Ueber die Einwirkung verschiedner Gasse und des luftverdünnten Raumes auf die Bewegungerscheinungen im Pflanzenreich. Bot. Zeit. 20:341–348.

KERNER, A. 1876. Die Schlussmittel der Blüten gegen unberufene Gäste.

——— and OLIVER, F. W. 1895. The natural history of plants.

KIENHOLZ, R. 1927. Shrinkage and growth in plant stems. Bot. Gaz. 83:103–105.

KOSTYTSCHEW, S. 1926. Lehrbuch der Pflanzenphysiologie.

KÜSTER, E. 1927. Beiträge zur Kenntnis der Plasmolyse. Protoplasma. 1:73–104.

LEPESCHKIN, W. W. 1908. Zur Kenntnis des Mechanismus der photonastischen Variationsbewegungen und der Einwirkung des Beleuchtungswechsels auf die Plasmamembran. Beih. Bot. Centralbl. 24:308–356.

LINNÉ, C. 1751. Philosophia Botanica.

LUNDEGÅRDH, H. 1922. Eine Beiträge zur quantitativen Analyse des Phototropismus. Arkiv. Bot. 18:1–62.

MacDOUGAL, D. T. 1920. Hydration and growth.

MOLISCH, H. 1923. Mikrochemie der Pflanzen.

MOLZ, F. J. 1926. A study of suction force by a simplified method. 1. Effect of experimental factors. Am. Jour. Bot. 13:433–501.

NIGEL, B. B. 1926. Transmission of stimuli in plants. Nature. 118:589–590.

NUERNBERGK, E. 1925. Beiträge zur Physiologie des Tagesschlafs der Pflanzen.

OLTMANNS, F. 1895. Ueber das Öffnen und Schliessen der Blüten. Bot. Zeit. 53:31-52.

OPDENBOSCH, M. 1924. Action de la lumière et de la chaleur sur l'ouverture et la fermeture des fleurs. Acad. Roy. Belgique Bull. 18–30.

PALLADIN, V. I. and LIVINGSTON, B. E. 1922. Plant physiology.

PFEFFER, W. 1873. "Herr Dr. Pfeffer hält einen Vortrag über Oeffnen und Schliessen der Blüthen." Bot. Zeit. 31:239–240, 247–250.
———. 1873. Physiologische Untersuchungen.
———. 1875. Die periodischen Bewegungen der Blattorgane.
———. 1907. Untersuchungen über die Entstehung der Schlafbewegungen der Blattorgane. Abh. König. Sächs. Ges. Wiss. 30:257–472.
———. 1911. Der Einfluss von mechanischer Hemmung und von Belastung auf der Schlafbewegungen.
———. 1915. Beiträge zur Kenntnis der Entstehung der Schlafbewegungen. Abh. König. Sächs. Ges. Wiss. 34:1–154.
PRANCHARD, T. L. and WAIGHT, F. M. O. 1923. On the presentation time and the latent time for reaction to gravity in Pteridophytes. Rep. Brit. Ass. 1922 and Ann. Bot. 37:55–61.
PRINGSHEIM, E. G. 1912. Die Reizbewegungen der Pflanzen.
ROMELL, L. 1918. Zur Frage einer Reizbarkeit blütender Zellen durch hydrostatischen Druck. Sven. Bot. Tids. 12:338–361.
ROYER, M. CH. 1868. Essai sur le sommeil des plantes. Ann. Sci. Nat. Bot. 9:345–379.
SACHS, J. 1857. Ueber das Bewegungsorgan und die periodischen Bewegungen der Blätter von Phaseolus und Oxalis. Bot. Zeit. 15:792–802, 809–815.
———. 1863. Die voübergehenden Starre-Zustände periodisch beweglicher und reizbarer Pflanzenorgane. Flora. 46:449–459, 465–472, 481–489, 497–506.
———. 1863. Flora 46:449.
———. 1874. Lehrbuch der Botanik. 4 Aufl.
———. 1882. Textbook of Botany.
———. 1887. Lectures on the physiology of plants.
SAXTON, W. T. 1923. Some observations and suggestions regarding "nyctinasty." Jour. Ind. Bot. 3:127–142.
SCHWEIDLER, E. and SPERLICH, A. 1922. Die Bewegung der Primärblätter bei etiolierten Keimpflanzen von Phaseolus multiflorus. Zeits. Bot. 14:577–597.
SCHULZ, H. 1921. Über Korrelationen zwischen den Blütenteile und den geotropischen Bewegungen der Blütenschafter, nach Untersuchungen insbesondere an Papaver. Jahrb. Wiss. Bot. 60:1–66.
SKENE, M. 1924. The biology of flowering plants.
SNOW, R. 1924. Conduction of excitation in stem and leaf of Mimosa pudica. Roy. Soc. Proc. B. 96:349–374.
———. 1925. Conduction of excitation in the leaf of Mimosa spegazzini. Proc. Roy. Soc. London B. 98:188–201.
STERN, K. and BÜNNING, E. 1929. Über die tagesperiodischen Bewegungen der Primärblätter von Phaseolus multiflorus. I. Der Einfluss der Temperatur auf die Bewegungen. Ber. Deut. Bot. Ges. 47:565–583.
STILES, W. 1925. Irritability and movement in plants. Sci. Prog. 20:44–49.
STOPPEL, R. 1910. Über den Einfluss des Lichtes auf das Öffnen und Schliessen einiger Blüten. Zeit. Bot. 2:369–399.
———. 1916. Die Abhängigkeit der Schlafbewegungen von Phaseolus multiflorus von verschiedenen Aussenfaktoren. Zeits. Bot. 8:609–684.
———. 1920. Die Pflanzen in ihrer Beziehung zur atmosphärischen Elektrizität. Zeits. Bot. 12:529–575.
———. 1926. Die Schlafbewegungen der Blätter von Phaseolus multiflorus in Island zur Zeit der Mitternachtsonne. Zeits. wiss. Biol. Abt. E. Planta. 2:342–355.
——— and KNEIP, H. 1910. Weitere Untersuchungen über das Öffnen und Schliessen einiger Blüten. Zeits. Bot. 3:369–399.
——— and TRUMPF, C. 1922. Beiträge zum Problem der Schlafbewegungen von Phaseolus multiflorus. Mitt. Inst. Allg. Bot. Hamburg. 5:1–16.
STRASBURGER, E., JOST, L., SCHENCK, H. and KARSTEN, G. 1912. Textbook of Botany.
SUESSENGUTH, K. 1922. Untersuchungen über Variationsbewegungen von Blättern.
TRUMPF, C. 1924. Über den Einfluss intermittierender Beleuchtung auf des Etiolement der Pflanzen. Bot. Archiv. 5:381–410.
ULRICH, B. S. 1911. Leaf movements in the family Oxalidaceae. Cont. Bot. Lab. Univ. Pa. 3:211–242.
URSPRUNG, A. 1923. Unsere gegenwärtige Kenntnis über die osmotischen Zustandsgrössen der Pflanzenzelle. Verh. Naturf. Ges. Basel. 35:11–128.
——— and BLUM, G. 1916. Über die periodischen Schwankungen des osmotischen Wertes. Ber. Deut. Bot. Ges. 34:105–142.
———, ———. 1924. Eine Methode zur Messung des Wand- und Turgordruckes der Zelle, nebst Anwendungen. Jahrb. Wiss. Bot. 63:1–110.

VERWORN, M. 1912. Irritability.

VÖCHTING, H. 1882. Die Bewegungen der Blüten und Früchte.

——. 1890. Ueber den Einfluss der Wärme auf die Blütenbewegungen der Anemone stellata. Jahrb. Wiss. Bot. 21:285–297.

——. 1908. Untersuchungen zur experimentellen Anatomie und Pathologie des Pflanzenkörpers.

WALTER, H. 1924. Plasmaquellung und Wachstum. Zeits. Bot. 16:353–417.

WIEDERSHEIM, W. 1904. Studien über photonastische und thermonastische Bewegungen. Jahrb. Wiss. Bot. 40:230–278.

WIELER, A. 1893. Das Blüten der Pflanzen. Beit. biol. Pflanzen 6:1–211.

WIGGANS, R. G. 1921. Variations in the osmotic concentrations of the guard cells during the opening and closing of stomata. Am. Jour. Bot. 8:30–40.

WORTMANN, J. 1889. Beiträge zur Physiologie des Wachstums. Bot. Zeit. 47:229–239, 245–253, 261–272, 277–288, 293–304.